Feasible Socialism
The National Health Service, past, present & future

Julian Tudor Hart
MB BChir DCH FRCP FRCGP

with illustrations by the author

Feasible Socialism: The National Health Service, past, present and future by Julian Tudor Hart

First published by the Socialist Health Association
16 Charles Square, London N1 6HP

ISBN 0 900687 24X

Contents

*F*oreword

The first aim of this book is to provide an easily readable, referenced account of how the National Health Service (NHS) developed from 1948 to the market "reforms" of 1989, and how it might resume progress as a democratised public service. A secondary aim is to convince a new generation of health workers, and others seriously concerned with the NHS, that they need to do more than merely hold good opinions. Something must be done, with urgency and intelligence, together with others who share our concern. The Socialist Health Association (formerly the Socialist Medical Association) was a great force in the past, and could be in the future for the next generation. The Labour movement needs the SHA as an independenent Socialist conscience. But we first need to understand the new world we live in, where it came from, and where we must go.

The book raises four fundamentally important issues.

First, despite being given free to the whole population according to need, by doctors and nurses with scarcely a notion of what anything cost, the NHS provided more cost-effective public service than any of its fee-paid or insurance-based international competitors. We seemed, almost inadvertently, to have discovered a cash-free economy which was both popular and effective.

Secondly, the attempt since 1989 to purge the NHS of these social elements, and force it into the mould of industrial commodity production, has shaken the service from top to bottom. Here and there this shaking-up has created new opportunities for long-overdue innovation, but its more general effects have been to inflate management costs, demoralise much of the NHS workforce, and accelerate a socially irresponsible shift from continuing labour-intensive care, to episodic technology-intensive "cure". There is no evidence of any of the improved cost-effectiveness predicted by its promoters and apologists, and every reason to believe that costs will continue to escalate.

Thirdly, vesting all public responsibility for personal care in professionals effectively accountable to nobody, without which the NHS could probably not have been born in 1948, must now be recognised as having become a fundamental constraint on future progress. Accountability to appointed, unelected managers has been a disaster. Health workers must be accountable to someone; why not to the people they serve? A critical mass of both health professionals and the public are now ready for a new era in health care, the transformation of patients from an essentially passive status as consumers, to become active co-producers of health gain. This sometimes glib concept could become an extremely powerful idea if it were translated into specific, concrete, practical clinical terms. This would open up new perspectives for local participative democracy which could begin to undo the damage done to the NHS by aggressive managerialism, without returning to the complacent stagnation of unaccountable professionalism.

Fourthly and finally, these conclusions suggest that when the NHS resumes its natural advance as a socialised, locally accountable public service, it may have more to teach Britain's disintegrating industrial base, than to learn from it. By suggesting new ways in which common ownership of the means of production, distribution and exchange might be realised, other than through centralised control in a bureaucratic state, clause four of the Labour Party's Constitution could become a means of escape from the idiot-logic of production for profit, rather than an embarrassing anachronism.

To keep the book short enough for a mass readership, many important topics have been dealt with summarily, or not at all. The most important of these is the pharmaceutical industry, and other for-profit industries supplying the NHS. This is such a large and important subject in its own right, and so long overdue for fundamental re-evaluation from a principled Socialist standpoint, that it really requires another book in its own right. Further reading on most other topics is indicated in the references.

This book could not have appeared without the generous imagination of the Central Council of the Socialist Health Association, particularly Doug Naysmith, Tony Jewell, Christine Hogg and Joy Mostyn. I am also grateful to my former partner Dr Brian Gibbons for encouragement, and critical reading of early drafts.

Julian Tudor Hart

This book is dedicated to the memory of Dr Hugh Faulkener, 1912-1994, chairman of the Medical Practitioners' Union, lifelong supporter of the SHA, and unacknowledged principal author of the 1966 general practitioners' Charter, the most (many might say the only) successful reform of the NHS since 1948.

PART ONE: THE PAST

"I need not remind you that what we get into scrapes for is not for saying what nobody believes and everybody says, but for saying what everybody believes and nobody says."

Florence Nightingale. Letter to Sir John McNeill, 1857.

1

Origins of the National Health Service

Ideas about a National Health Service (NHS) have been around ever since the French revolution. The Jacobins predicted an end to all disease as soon as everyone was well fed, housed and educated, as they believed would occur soon after the world became ruled by reason. Like all revolutionaries, they saw remote ends more clearly than immediately feasible means, but their perception that most disease and premature death was rooted in poverty has provided the rational foundation for public health policy ever since.

In the Victorian era, Sir John Simon tried to set up a unified national medical service, not just to tinker with disease, but to maintain public health. He was easily isolated by his clinical colleagues, who lived from sale of their skills, real or imagined, not from enlightened government. A main function of all trade unions was mutual assistance in times of illness, often with some elementary provision for prepaid medical care on the club system. These two elements, state-funded public health from above and *ad hoc* general practitioner (GP) care from below, eventually became the main points of origin for the NHS.

The idea got going again in the 20th century, when the South African war revealed that few British working men had been well enough fed to make good soldiers. The intoxication of empire, and new confidence that doctors might become men of science rather than shopkeepers, led to demands for health services to maintain the British race where God apparently wished it to be; firmly on top of everyone else. This ugly set of ideas attracted not only imperial Tories, but many medical intellectuals convinced they could design a more perfect human race in their own image. It ended in Auschwitz, but British doctors contributed to its origins, showing that medical professionalism, at least as traditionally understood, was no guarantee of humane thought and action.

The first modern proposals for a state medical service were presented by Fabians Sydney and Beatrice Webb in their Minority Report on the Poor Law in 1909. Churchill's description of Beatrice as a lady determined to scrub working class women into healthy behaviour had some justification. The Webbs shared some of the imperial and authoritarian delusions of their time, which may have helped to make them uncritical of Soviet communism in 1935. They showed little of the warmth and compassion of that other eminent Fabian, George Bernard Shaw. His description of the gap between teaching hospital theory and social reality has never been bettered[1]:

"The only way [a doctor for poor people] can preserve his self respect is by forgetting all he ever learnt of science, and clinging to such help as he can give without cost merely by being less ignorant and more accustomed to sick-beds than his patients. Finally he acquires a certain skill at nursing cases under poverty-stricken conditions, just as women who have been trained as domestic servants in some huge institution with lifts, vacuum cleaners, electric lighting, steam heating, and machinery that turns the kitchen into a laboratory and engine-house combined, manage, when they are sent out into the world to drudge as general servants, to pick up their business in a new way, learning the slatternly habits and wretched makeshifts of homes where even bundles of kindling wood are luxuries to be anxiously economised."

That description still fitted the situation that I, and thousands of other young GPs like me, found in inner-London practice when I qualified in 1952.

By 1911, Lloyd George was on his way to becoming the most cunning and effective prime minister our ruling class ever had since Disraeli. He saw that industrial workers, till then the mass base of the Liberal Party, were moving toward Socialism and the new Labour Party, and similar changes were accelerating all over the world. In Germany, Chancellor Bismarck had tamed revolutionary Socialism by introducing state medical insurance. Lloyd George took a look, and came back with similar proposals for Britain. His 1911 Insurance Act was the origin of the Welfare State, and his nationalisation of club medicine and local insurance in 1912 was the progenitor of the NHS in 1948[2].

The heart of this service was not medical care, but cash benefits to breadwinners during episodes of sickness or injury, to keep families from pauperism and maintain a viable labour force for industry. From the point of view of the state, GPs were involved mainly as judges of entitlement to benefit; any medical care they gave was an incidental bonus. To the extent that effective medical science was applied at all, it was assumed to exist only in hospitals, an attitude that continued well into the 1960s.

In the same year of 1912 the State Medical Service Association was formed, to press for the Lloyd George Insurance Act to be further developed into an NHS, including hospital care in a comprehensive service. In 1929 it renamed itself the National Medical Service Association, and in 1931 it became the Socialist Medical Association, affiliated to the Labour Party. From then on it campaigned first to establish, later to maintain and defend "a Socialised Medical Service, both preventive and curative, free, and open to all". In 1982 it again renamed itself as the Socialist Health Association. Many different forces influenced the NHS we actually got in 1948, but the SHA was certainly one of them[3].

Birth of the National Health Service

The war in the West became serious in 1940. On the brink of defeat and all-too-possible Nazi occupation, Britain was forced to look at itself honestly. Like other important national industries, hospitals were found to be grossly underfunded, unplanned, unco-ordinated, irrationally distributed, and under-equipped. Few had laboratory or X-ray services, and most relied on GP-surgeons plus a few unpaid consultants who worked free, in exchange for a secure base for private practice.

Right-wing Conservatives, the Thatcherites of their day, had admired the fascist dictators' success in suppressing independent trade unions and socialist ideas. This underlay Chamberlain's policy of appeasement. Together with years of mass unemployment, the undeniable consequences of appeasement of fascism marginalised the Conservative right for an entire generation. Alliance with the USSR, which bore the brunt of the fighting, and the excellent results of state planning for British war industry, created a wider social base for socialist ideas than ever before or since.

Swept along on this tidal wave of commitment to a new and better post-war world, in 1944 the British Medical Association (BMA) collaborated in government plans for a future National Health Service. It was a high point in popular resolve never to return to pre-war *laissez faire* economic policies and their consequent high unemployment and social division, finally expressed in the landslide election of 1945 and Britain's first majority Labour government. By then the BMA and Conservative Party were in full retreat from NHS plans they had endorsed a year earlier. Without a Labour government, no comprehensive NHS would have been born; at best, we would have had a two-tier service, with private insurance at the top and poor care for poor people at the bottom.

Birth of the NHS required not just a Labour government, but a Socialist vision of the future. Almost single-handed, Aneurin Bevan was the architect of the NHS. He grew up in a coal-mining village, where people learned through bitter experience to share forms of wealth that were indivisible, and to respect values that were unmarketable. He wrote only one short book on his ideas about Socialism, *In Place of Fear*[4]. The fears he had in mind were those the 1945 Labour government tried to delete from British society: of losing jobs, homes, health, and personal dignity, fears which threatened and often blighted the lives of most working people between the two world wars.

Despite huge advances in medical care, we still fear the natural consequences of ill-health with good reason; but for more than 40 years since 1948, nobody in Britain has had to fear its *un*natural consequences despite a market economy; mounting bills from doctors and hospitals, and insurance premiums that rise with risk, and never cover all the most serious contingencies, and the unspeakable question hovering over every commercial transaction — is this to help me or to help him?

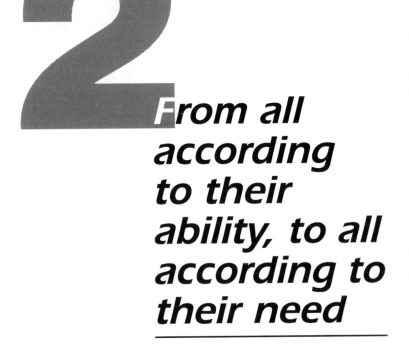

2 From all according to their ability, to all according to their need

The NHS guaranteed all necessary and effective treatment and care free to the whole population as a human right, regardless of tax or insurance status, funded from taxation, limited only by what medical science made possible, and what the nation as a whole could afford. Persuading people to share equally in adversity has never been a problem, in Britain or anywhere else. Difficulties begin when they must be persuaded to accept poverty for themselves, side by side with visible extravagance for their "betters". Talk about "rationing" in such circumstances is at best confusing, at worst hypocrisy. Compared with today, Britain in 1948 was a poor country; food was still rationed tighter than during the war, one fifth of our housing stock was destroyed by enemy action, and all our basic industries were clapped out from years of taking out profits without forward investment in equipment or staff training.

By 1948 the leaders of the BMA were denouncing the proposed NHS as a monstrous intrusion by government into their private world of doctor-patient relationships, conscription of an honourable profession to a subordinate role as powerless civil servants. They were supported by the Conservative Party, which voted against the NHS Bill at its second and third readings in parliament in 1946, and voted again against implementation of the Act in February 1948.

Despite Bevan's repeated guarantees of clinical autonomy for both family doctors and specialists, and a massive majority in favour of the NHS Act in parliament, the BMA chose defence of "clinical freedom" as its rallying cry for opposition to the new service. One BMA leader described the NHS as "a step toward Nazism as practised in Hitler's Germany"[5]. Only four months before the NHS was due to start in 1948, the BMA was still refusing even to negotiate with the Minister, a stand endorsed by 9 out of 10 GPs on an 84% vote. BMA chairman Dr Guy Dain declared:

> "The Act is a paper service and nothing more. The people who have been promised a free-for-all service available to everybody are going to be very disappointed. The service will not and cannot be there on 5th July or any reasonably approximate date ... The failure of the service must recoil on the people who produced it well knowing that it was impossible to implement"[6].

A new path entirely

Referring to such attitudes among the majority of doctors, Bevan's speech in parliament is worth quoting:

> "I think it is a sad reflection that this great Act, to which every Party has made its contribution, in which every section of the community is vitally interested, should have so stormy a birth. I should have thought, and we all hoped, that they would have realised that we are setting their feet on a new path entirely, that

we ought to take pride in the fact that, despite our financial and economic anxieties, we are still able to do the most civilised thing in the world — put the welfare of the sick in front of every other consideration."

Two months after the appointed day, 93% of the population was enrolled, reaching 97% by the end of the year. In spite of themselves, the doctors' feet were indeed set on a new path entirely. They learned from their own experience that release from fee-earning improved rather than impaired doctor-patient relationships. Public service enabled them to serve more people more effectively, at lower cost to the nation, with greater personal security and integrity than they ever had in private practice. By the end of the 1960s most were supporting the NHS as vigorously as they had once opposed it, and so they have remained.

A socialised service that worked

From the beginning, Conservatives denounced the whole idea of a free service as utopian and unworkable, a violation of human nature, and a sure road to bankruptcy. According to them, wherever the state undertook to provide what might otherwise have been produced and sold for profit by entrepreneurs, unit costs and bureaucratic overheads would rise, quality would fall, and personal responsibility would disappear. Administrative costs were bound to soar and efficiency bound to decline. Wherever medical care was still sold as a commodity, it fetched a high price in the market, at least from those who could afford it; so at zero price demand would be infinite. Wherever suppliers were guaranteed support from the state, they produced regardless of cost, so professional demands would be limitless.

Experience proved all these forecasts wrong. Although all medical care was completely free until 1952, and prescription charges from 1952 to 1979[1] were too low to have much deterrent effect, zero prices did not lead to infinite demand. This could have been anticipated by anyone who understood that medical care incurs human costs even at zero price (going to a doctor is not like eating ice cream) and that professional claims that medical care was not just a business were not wholly hypocritical. **Appendices 1 and 2** show how Britain compared with other economically developed countries for total health service costs as a percentage of Gross National Product, and the percentage of health service costs borne by public expenditure, in 1975 and in 1987, just before NHS "reform" pushed us back to the marketplace.

Appendices 1 and 2 suggest that the more medical care is socialised and freely accessible to all of the people, the cheaper it is to provide. Comparing the UK, where 87% of all spending on medical care was met by the state, with the USA, where the state met only 41% of costs[7], total medical spending in Britain was about half as much as a proportion of GNP, and about one quarter as much per head of population. Other countries in this table showed less dramatic contrasts, but generally followed the same pattern.

There are simple and obvious reasons for this. Once any service is made freely available to the entire population as a human right, it is cheaper to give than to sell. No one has to be employed to collect the money, to make sure nobody gets care without paying for it, or to promote the product to maintain profits. Nobody has to collect profits, opportunities for fraud are minimised, and (though this is unimaginable to anti-Socialists) many if not most people work more conscientiously in a public service run to meet serious human needs, than for managers running a business for profit.

Despite cocksure predictions of inflated bureaucracy in the socialised NHS, this never occurred until Conservative "reforms" began forcing the NHS back to the marketplace in 1990. Within a broad

national plan for rational distribution and integration of specialist facilities, and for equal distribution of general practitioners (both largely achieved in the first 20 years), clinicians were allowed to develop their work in their own way, with minimal interference from management. Administrative costs were consequently small, running at about 2% of all NHS costs in the first two decades, and about 6% after the reorganisation of 1974. Compare this with administrative costs of about 23% of all spending on medical care in the state-subsidised competitive market in USA[8], where even after the Clinton reforms, each doctor will relate to ten or more different insurance agencies, and each claim for fees must be verified. Predictably, since managed competition was imposed on the NHS by Conservative "reform", administrative costs have risen, from about 6% of NHS costs when Thatcher came to power in 1979, to nearly 11% in 1994, and are still rising. Between 1987 and 1993, years of the "reform", total administrative costs more than doubled, from £1.44 bn a year to just over £3 bn. Over the same years, senior management costs rose from £25.7m to £494m.[9] Because of the lack of accountability enjoyed by consultants and GPs in the old NHS, it was under-managed. Serious planning, based on evidence from good information systems, requires staff who must be paid, and a reasonable rise in costs was necessary and justifiable; but this is not what happened in the internal market. Middle management in private industry expects annual incomes over £100,000, and senior management starts at £300,000. Remodelling the NHS on business lines has incurred wholly unnecessary costs, which have damaged morale throughout the service.

3 Under-provision and oversale

Predictions of extravagance and bureaucracy having failed, the next line of argument was that though the NHS might indeed be cheap at the price, this was only because it didn't deliver the goods. Potentially unlimited demand for free medical care in the NHS had to be limited in practice by long waiting lists unknown in marketed medical care systems; and when patients finally got care, it was of inferior quality.

Nobody doubts that waiting lists were indeed used to discourage demand, though that doesn't prove that demand would have been infinite without them. Part-time consultants always had a cash incentive to maintain long NHS waiting lists; how else could they ensure full bookings for their private clinics? This fact, known to every patient who ever asked their GP if a private consultation would short-cut the waiting list, could always have been verified by politicians, simply by comparing waiting lists of full-time and part-time consultants. No such study was ever commissioned by any Health Minister. It is hard to avoid the conclusion that waiting lists were a convenient brake on demand for specialist care in NHS hospitals, and were tolerated for no other reason. Had any Ministers been seriously concerned to abolish waiting lists, they would have collected meaningful data centrally. In fact, the only data collected and discussed related to delays between seeing a specialist and admission to hospital; the even more significant delays between GP referral and seeing a specialist (in my part of South Wales, commonly three months or so, occasionally two or three years) were neither collated nor discussed in parliament[10]. Local figures existed, because they were circulated by health authorities to GPs, presumably in the justified hope that many referrals might be thereby discouraged as more or less futile, but these figures were not gathered centrally. Of course, these delays cost lives[11]. Even if cases marked "urgent" were seen sooner (and there is still no consistent policy on this), they had first to be recognised as such by GPs.

The NHS was *never* adequately funded by any government, Labour or Conservative. There were always other, more pressing demands on public spending, whether clinging to empire, stoking up the fires of the cold war, repaying the gnomes of Zürich, or reducing tax-burdens on the rich.

Underfunding in a state service is not inevitable. Nobody expects a poor nation to provide a rich service, but like the health workers it employs, it should do the best it can with the resources available. We can and should demand that if our country can produce so many non-essential consumer goods that an army of advertisers and salesmen must persuade us to buy them, we can certainly afford to pay for the rational application of medical science to basic human needs. The level of state funding depends on real rather than rhetorical social priorities. If sufficient private wealth exists for the whole population to pay individually for medical services in the market, it must exist also as a potential tax base for services to be paid for collectively, at lower cost and with greater efficiency.

Even with long in-patient and out-patient waiting lists (in my own experience, up to three years for one specialty, where the same consultant could be seen privately in a few days), NHS specialists were eventually accessible to the whole population. Virtually everyone was registered with a family doctor to provide primary care, and to act as informed advocate to get specialist care. Not so in the USA, where despite spending four times more per head on health care, 15% of US citizens had access only to hospital emergency rooms, another 30% had insufficient insurance to cover major illness, and even the highest payers could not get more than 80% cover for catastrophic illness. As for family doctors, they earned so much less than specialists that they almost disappeared, and are now having to be expensively re-invented.

However, it is still true that cheaper care in the NHS also meant less care, even if spread more justly throughout our population. **Figure 1** compares rates in the UK and USA for some common surgical procedures.

Figure 1. Admission rates per 1000 population for operations on tonsils, gall bladder, inguinal hernia, prostate and uterus, UK and USA, 1980.

	Tonsil	Gall bladder	Inguinal hernia	Prostate	Uterus
UK	26	78	154	144	250
USA	205	203	238	308	557

From McPherson K. International differences in medical care practices. In: OECD Social Policy Studies No.7 *Health care systems in transition.* Paris: OECD 1990, Table 3, p.22

There is no evidence of large differences in prevalence of illness to account for these huge differences in surgical activity. Rates might be too low in the UK, too high in USA, or both. However that may be, they give no support to charges of extravagance against the NHS, and in fact an independent enquiry set up by the first post-war Conservative administration (the Guillebaud Commission) concluded that:

"Any charge that there is widespread extravagance in the National Health Service, whether in respect of the spending of money or the use of manpower, is not borne out by our evidence ... we have found no opportunity for making recommendations which would either produce new sources of income or reduce in substantial degree the annual cost of the Service. In some instances — and particularly with regard to the level of hospital capital expenditure — we have found it necessary, in the interests of the future efficiency of the Service, to make recommendations which will tend to increase the future cost."

This scotched the charge of NHS extravagance, though none of those who forecast this ever admitted their error; and it confirmed chronic underfunding. It therefore implied the probability of some underprovision in the NHS, and there has in fact been good evidence that some interventions, notably coronary bypass grafts and kidney dialysis, have been underprovided, particularly for older people. There were also gross delays for some routine operations like cholecystectomy (removal of the gallbladder), operations for cataract, and hip joint replacement. For technical interventions as a whole, the issue is less simple than it is often made to appear, because professional attitudes to treatment are generally less aggressive in Britain than the USA, a view often shared by patients. Attitudes are certainly biased by the pressures of contrasting care systems, the NHS toward complacency and low taxes, the US medical market toward sales promotion and high fees.

Despite large differences before the war, since the NHS there was no evidence of within-region social differences for any common surgical procedures up to 1985[12]. In their family doctors, all NHS patients had potential informed advocates, most of whom evidently maintained enough pressure to prevent social bias in distribution of services, and ensure that priority went to need rather than status. This was an important social gain, and suggests that professional integrity not only survived, but grew in a socialised service. In marketed care in the USA, on the other hand, there was evidence of gross overprovision for the rich and underprovision for the poor for both

coronary bypass grafts[13] and caesarean section[14]. Higher professional groups[15], and higher earners[16], got more elective surgery. There are some prosperous areas of the US with evidence of only minimal social gradients for surgical process[17], so economic pressures are not the only determinants of professional behaviour, but they are bound to favour wealthier consumers in a free market.

Overprovision of medical or surgical interventions may be as dangerous to health as underprovision. No care system can of itself ensure appropriate care, which depends on clinical judgement and professional integrity. There will be some lazy doctors and some greedy ones in any system; but to give doctors economic incentives to remove parts of our bodies or interfere with our natural chemistry seems almost as silly as paying to have our brains washed by Rupert Murdoch's newspapers.

Even in fee-earning systems, it is unlikely that most doctors work consistently to maximise income rather than improve patient care, though a few certainly do. More commonly they, like other entrepreneurs, complacently assume that their own and their customers' interests coincide. United States doctors are about twice as likely to remove a uterus as doctors in the NHS, but as they recommend this for their wives even more often than for their other patients their beliefs are honestly held[18]. Once doctors are paid according to production not of better health outcomes, but of processes assumed to result in those outcomes, the stage is set for clinical inflation, because the market rewards credulity and penalises scepticism.

4 Choking their mouths with power

Greed is a powerful but dangerous fuel for social machinery. Popular experience of the NHS soon taught us that a care system with an internal economy of gift relationships could cost less and operate with greater social justice and efficiency than care systems based on selling medical care as a commodity. By the 1960s a socialised NHS had become an apparently irreversible part of popular British culture, a consensus that had to be shared even by Conservative politicians if they wanted to get elected.

When Bevan laid the foundations of the NHS, he had more respect for doctors than they had for him. Once liberated from pursuit of fees, he trusted them to temper clinical optimism with scientific scepticism, to become less credulous than the general public about the effectiveness of medical and surgical interventions, and more cautious about the human costs of care, both in terms of professional workload, and risks of harmful side-effects and clinical accidents. This attitude seems to have prepared him for what can now be seen as a historic compromise with medical autonomy. Despite overall elected political control from the Ministry of Health, aimed mainly at geographical redistribution of resources, the pace and direction of NHS development was left almost entirely in the hands of senior consultant physicians and surgeons. The most important quality apparently sought in members appointed (not elected) to NHS regional authorities and hospital boards seemed to be ability to get on with senior doctors.

Doctors, nurses, and the many paramedical professions around them, were traditionally "non-political" pillars of established authority. Their conservatism made it easy to assimilate the socialised NHS into British consensus politics, although the American Medical Association continued to denounce it as communism, a not unreasonable description of a system in which wealth was distributed according to need, and nobody knew the price of anything.

Karl Marx's principle of the "highest form of Socialism", "from all according to their ability, to all according to their need"[19], was realised in practice in the NHS, but modified in one vital respect; doctors were the sole judges of both ability and need. Other than their own, whose interests would this self-regulating profession represent? Initially, the rich and powerful could count on instinctive loyalty from the top doctors who had always dominated medical culture not only in their own sectional interest, but in the more general interests of a stable social hierarchy guaranteeing them high status. But in the longer run, none of these assumptions was secure, because medicine is science-led, is now wholly dependent on the continued existence of a state-funded service, and is now developing the same relationships as in other forms of production; the age of the self-employed doctor is over. As the professional hierarchy shifted from aristocracy to meritocracy, the power and influence of doctors came more and more to depend on their work rather than their wealth and connections, and their continued support for the ruling few came to depend on continued provision of public service in their interest.

Convergence of medical science with medical practice

It is generally agreed by historians that not until the early years of the 20th century did all medical and surgical interventions put together even begin to save more lives than they destroyed. Substantial net saving of life began only about 1935, with introduction of sulphonamide antibiotics. At the time of the Lloyd George Act, treatment consisted of a great deal of heavy nursing, millions of gallons of often toxic but almost entirely ineffective medicines, and desperate ventures into abdominal and obstetric surgery when there seemed to be no alternative. At the birth of the NHS in 1948, effective medical treatment was just reaching take-off speed, with penicillin introduced generally in 1944, and the first antibiotics effective against tuberculosis in 1950. Surgery was changing from a last resort to a routine assumption, but only for conditions where life seemed impossible or intolerable without it. As always, nursing care was real and effective, but relatively unchanging and predictable in cost. Medical care, on the other hand, was rapidly shifting from dominant illusion sustained by scraps of reality, to dominant reality contaminated by residual illusion. A political decision to guarantee universal free care today would be a lot bolder than it seemed in 1948.

Like other sciences, medical science began with description, followed by experiment, and only much later by intervention with more or less predictable results. Except for a handful serving the top of society, doctors had little social authority or status until the late 19th century, when the evident future promise of medical science began to make it more credible than religion. Modern medical culture, and the social characteristics of medical professionalism, date from that time, when medical science promised much, but actually delivered almost nothing in terms of personal care for disease. It had real achievements, but these lay almost entirely in the field of public health, not personal clinical care. Medical wealth, and therefore power, was concentrated in personal clinical care for top people, not public health for the nation. The terms of medical professionalism were therefore the terms of medical trade, made credible by association with medical science, but certainly not based on it.

In its relations with other health workers and with patients, medical trade (and therefore medical professionalism) depended on maximising the power and authority of doctors, and minimising those of everyone else. Technical interventions had almost no positive effect on outcomes of illness before about 1910, began to be appreciable around 1935, and became dominant from the 1950s onward, but they were not the sole content of care. Even by 1991, David Eddy, professor of health policy and management at Duke University North Carolina, estimated that only about 15% of clinical interventions were fully supported by good scientific evidence[20]; we are still much closer to the beginning than we like to think. Apart from nursing, the real and apparent effects on illness of reassurance, hope, and faith in one's doctor, what is now called the placebo effect, was originally the main content of all treatments. It remains important enough today to be taken into account in all scientific studies (a fact which in no way invalidates science, but simply confirms that what goes on in our brains does, not surprisingly, affect the function of subordinate organs[21]). Doctors, patients, and all other paramedical health workers recognised this, and all of them (not just doctors) conspired to preserve and if possible magnify this effect, through a culture of secrecy, well-intended lying, and contrived optimism, all contradicting every principle of science.

Technological advance precedes cultural advance. The autonomous medical profession whose work was socialised by the NHS in 1948 still clung to this anti-scientific culture, but their credibility, to themselves and to society, already depended on the most rigorous application of critical scientific method, in a state of free international intellectual competition which soon eliminated the self-deceiving customs of the past, at least at an academic level. As more and more of clinical medicine became real, there was less and less need for pretence. The new doctors understood biochemistry and elementary statistics, and welcomed their new opportunities to practice regardless of patients' means. They began to understand that without skilled paramedical teams they were powerless, and that most of the really big problems in medical care were insoluble without intelligent participation by patients both in diagnosis and treatment.

Between 1948, when the socialised NHS began, and 1989, when the first serious steps were taken to drag it back to the market, the British medical profession began a qualitative change, from systematic mystification and lying (mostly in the cause of hope and optimism) to systematic audit of the truth, from using science to being scientists. This change is still only beginning, but its direction is not in doubt. It may be delayed, but will not be changed by current attempts to corrupt medical science by commercialising the NHS. We can be sure of this, because even in the United States, with a health care system already corrupted by decades of commercialism and universities demoralised by visions of immensely profitable "intellectual property", the logic of medical science is creating internal criticism which must ultimately burst through the constraints of the market. More than any other group, doctors know not only what medical science makes possible, but also how little of this is effectively applied to the people as a whole. A body of intelligent men and women has been created whose work is vital to any society, and who know what can and should be done. Permanently to prevent them doing it for all because a few families must have three cars, a yacht and a swimming pool, is not possible.

What about the workers?

Doctors have been pushed a long way into understanding their own situation in society, but most are still far from understanding the pressures on other health workers, without whom modern medical practice is impossible.

Despite the behaviour of the BMA leaders, Bevan kept all his promises to the doctors, respecting not only their professional autonomy, but also defending the high incomes guaranteed to consultants by the notorious Distinction Awards system. He backed Lord Moran against attempts by Hugh Gaitskell, then Chancellor of the Exchequer, to reduce them. Neither Bevan nor any of his successors, Labour or Conservative, showed similar respect for other health workers. Having inherited a grossly underpaid nursing, domestic and ancillary workforce in 1948, the NHS faced a 22% rise in its wages bill in its first year, after conceding a 30% wage rise for nurses. From then on, Bevan put his full weight behind government demands for restraint and self-sacrifice for all other health workers[22].

Perhaps this was political realism, inevitable if the NHS was to be born at all; but if loyalty to doctors secured its birth, taking all other health workers for granted almost led to its death. The right of workers in public service to wages comparable with workers in commodity production was never willingly conceded by any government, Labour or Conservative. Year after year, nurses and other paramedical staff refused to take industrial action for wages comparable to those in commodity services and manufacturing, and saw themselves slip down the social ladder in consequence. The inevitable result of holding down wages for the lowest paid workers in essential public services was eventual confrontation[23]. In the 1978-79 "winter of discontent", the last Labour government used such waning energy as it had to keep hospital porters, domestic staff, dustmen and gravediggers where they had always been, at the bottom of society. Fifteen years of uninterrupted Conservative rule has followed. To find a way out of a deep hole, we need to think about how we fell in.

Medical autonomy took the rest of the medical team for granted. Roughly 10% of the workforce took all the decisions for everyone else. In other fields, socialists have painfully discovered that participative democracy is a not an option, but a necessity. Command socialism can build the primitive outlines of an industrial economy, but to get beyond that, people must be free to think and work for themselves in their own way, using their own brains. An economy fuelled by fear is even worse than one fuelled by greed, and the new social fuels we need for Socialism can't be developed in a barracks. Next time round, to go forward at all we must go together. The phrase "care team" must acquire real meaning, but working experience is doing just this. Unity across the whole spectrum of medical, paramedical, nursing and domestic staff will be difficult to achieve, but if we look thoughtfully at how effective health care must now be delivered through diverse but integrated care teams, a material rather than romantic basis for unity can be understood; in 1948 it was unthinkable.

What about the patients?

The autonomous medical profession could ignore any active role for patients even more easily than for other health workers. Doctors traditionally recognised two kinds of patient. Paying patients, like other customers, were always right and therefore had to be humoured. Non-paying, public service patients, were supposed to earn their right to care by having serious or at least interesting diseases, and to be grateful for getting any care at all; beggars can't be choosers.

The advent of the NHS, giving everyone a right to medical care whenever it was needed, paid for by everyone by taxes throughout their working lives, potentially created an entirely new situation. From 1948 onwards, the service belonged to the people, and so did its most skilled workers, since the substantial costs of training both doctors and nurses were borne almost entirely by the NHS and paid for by taxes, not tuition fees. But it took a long time for most patients to see it this way, and even longer for doctors. Until well into the 1980s, NHS patients were (by international standards) notoriously uncritical, so that (for example) even today, malpractice insurance cover for doctors can be about nine times less in the UK than in the USA. You complain about faulty goods you have bought, you don't complain about gifts.

An important reason the new radical Conservatives have, so far, got away with imposing market competition on the NHS, is that they recognised that patients were no longer prepared to be taken for granted by a state-funded charity, which seemed to advance only at a speed and in directions convenient and interesting for doctors, not patients. Forty years is a long time to go on feeling grateful for gifts you have already paid for with taxes. People are not all fools. They know very well that the charm of shop-assistants is superficial, motivated more by bonus payments for sales than by personal concern for the customer, but they prefer being valued only as consumers, to not being valued at all.

The nationalised health industry followed the same authoritarian pattern as other nationalised industries, conceived by socialists perhaps, but certainly not implemented by them. Like all the others, the nationalised health service was run not as a new kind of industry by the people, for the people, and of the people, but as the old kind of industrial dictatorship, without even the illusory democracy of consumer choice. Unlike other nationalised industries, however, the NHS despots were distributed non-hierarchically throughout its operative units, as clinically autonomous doctors, at a folksy level of despotism not entirely inaccessible to individual consumers. And so, when the rest of state capitalism crashed, the NHS did not. It had within itself the basis for future change, not back to the market, but up, out, and beyond anything the market could ever imagine.

PART TWO:
THE PRESENT

5 Consumerism, science, and the language of production

Margaret Thatcher almost completely succeeded in imposing her consumerist agenda on an entire political generation, across its whole spectrum from Left to Right. She succeeded not through any exceptional talent or imagination, but because her rediscovery of primitive 19th century *laissez-faire* economics coincided with the world-wide collapse of the only full scale socialist economies (real or imagined) history has so far produced. For the past decade at least, the market has swept the board.

In this view of the world, the large majority of ordinary people have either ceased to exist as producers, or will shortly do so. Whatever creative capacity they retain after 150 years of factory work will soon be replaced by machines, taking what were once fallible human decisions, more efficiently and therefore more profitably for managers and shareholders. Making money is the social justification for existence. Unless you can either employ others, or be employed yourself, with a profitable outcome, you are a burden on those who can.

Whereas your dignity and usefulness as a producer is therefore questionable and limited, your status as a consumer is assured, always assuming you have some money to spend. As a consumer, you are wooed day and night by half-naked ladies asking you to buy cars, dogs walking on the ceiling to sell you beer, and by housewives still wide-eyed and amazed after 50 years of beholding white getting whiter. As a voter, it seems less and less possible to change anything, but as a consumer, you can change anything for sale (that is, apparently everything) simply by purchasing one commodity rather than another. As a consumer, you have as many votes on how you will live, as you have money to spend on your choices. All you need is money, and all you need to get this is to forget about any other human objective, and concentrate on this single purpose. Then, legally or otherwise, you will almost certainly succeed, because even today few people are able to subordinate all other interests. To the extent that you get money, you become more of a winner and less of a loser, and thus edge your way nearer to the top of this great dung heap they have made of world history.

To see the alternative requires some imagination, and a lot of confidence that we are as yet using only a small fraction of human intelligence for any useful purpose. People acquire dignity and self-respect not as consumers, but as creative producers. Nowhere is this more true than in health care, and this truth is the key to the future of a socialist NHS.

When treatment seemed to depend largely on faith, medical care had the same immunity from serious criticism as religion. It was self-evidently good, and impious to suggest that its claims should be supported by serious evidence, so long as it remained doubtful whether much evidence existed. As reality displaced illusion in clinical interventions, and as state and corporate bulk purchasers replaced individual customers in medical trade, the processes of medical care began to be evaluated by the same criteria as other modes of production.

Socialists believe they can find better ways to organise society than to subordinate everyone and everything to pursuit of profit by a minority. To convince even ourselves, let alone others, we must accept evaluation of our ideas not in sentimental, romantic or religious terms of what should happen, but by rigorous measurement of what actually does happen. After a long experience of promises unfulfilled or contradicted, before anyone will risk losing what they already have, they want good evidence that change will be for the better. After 75 years of authoritarian Communism, and almost a hundred years of largely supine Social Democracy, no conspiracy is needed to discredit the very idea of Socialism (though such conspiracies do, of course, exist). The results of rigorous measurements will not always support our expectations. In any important activity, rigorous audit of what is actually going on virtually always produces initially disquieting results, showing that real performance falls below expected minimum standards. As Socialists are critical of things as they are and demand fundamental change, they should be confident that measured evidence will generally help them far more than their enemies.

For Socialists, it should therefore be easy to understand that it is a historic step forward to stop thinking of health care as an unverifiable (and therefore unfalsifiable) art, and begin thinking of it as a mode of production of value, whose objectives can be defined and efficiency in reaching them can be quantified. We can then begin to make medical practice as rational as the medical science on which it claims to be based.

In practice, many Socialists, and more so other progressives with less specific loyalties, do not welcome either the concept of medical care as a mode of production, or the convergence and eventual identity of medical practice with medical science. Previous generations of Socialists generally identified their own interests both with the progress of science, and the decline of superstition, in which they included most if not all religious belief. This is not true today, when science as a whole is seen as a more doubtful category, and religions are seen as something more than superstition. The relation of science to religion, and of both to socialist ideas, is an important question we cannot develop here, but its resolution probably depends at least partly on a redefinition of what we mean by science, how knowledge relates to doubt, how science relates to art (an antithesis between these two previously almost synonymous words began only in the early 19th century), how reason relates to faith, and how scientists themselves see their own social role.

In medical care in particular, both science and economics are mistrusted. Many progressive people are reluctant to abandon what was originally a strong cultural and political defence expressed in sentimental or religious terms, and prefer to exclude words like "production" and "efficiency" from any medical context, as a kind of blasphemy, accelerating the dehumanisation of medicine. The languages of science and health economics seem to them intrinsically dangerous, helping people to reach conclusions which were rightly unthinkable in the years of consensus.

Though no thinking person could fail to sympathise to some extent with these views, they are fundamentally wrong[24]. We shall make no serious headway against the marketing of medical care until we recognise that if we insist on using a pre-scientific language to discuss it, we limit ourselves to deploring a world we are no longer seriously trying to change. Of course figures can lie, because liars can figure, but if we refuse to define our terms, to count or to measure, liars have the field to themselves. As the evidence already quoted has shown, a socialist economy in the NHS, even of a most primitive kind, underfunded and hobbled by medical autonomy, was more cost-effective than marketed care in comparable societies, not marginally but by an order of magnitude. Providing all social costs and benefits are taken into account, not simply those agreeable to the accountants who now pass for health economists, and providing we make full allowance for the large but measurable uncertainties surrounding all calculations in human biology and sociology, we have nothing to fear and everything to gain from the most rigorous evaluation of all processes in the NHS, on essentially the same lines as other parts of the economy.

6 Consultations as units of production

The initial unit of medical production is the consultation, a meeting between a health professional on the one hand, and a person with problems on the other. All other main variable costs in the economy of all care systems originate from such consultations. In the NHS, with a simpler and more structured referral system than any other country, each series of clinical decisions leading ultimately to economically significant acts, for example cholecystectomy, hip replacements, kidney dialysis or coronary bypass grafts (four favourites for health economists), begins from a consultation between a patient and a health worker, usually a doctor.

The quality of decisions in these consultations is therefore critical for efficiency of the entire NHS. They determine how health problems are defined, and the nature of solutions sought. If things go wrong at this point, irrational costs ensue even if a specialist corrects them later.

Just as the shape of a large crystal depends on the exact configuration of its infinitesimally small component molecules, the nature of entire health care systems depends on the social relations of production in these consultations, how their objectives are defined, and how their limits are understood.

The conventional view of a consultation is that it is a transaction between a doctor-provider and a patient-consumer. In this view, transactions in doctors' shops are not fundamentally different from transactions in other shops. Health economists generally concede that consumers of medical care are even less able to behave as omniscient buyers in perfect markets, than other consumers of complex commodities. As few economists any longer believe that perfect markets, ideal buyers, or ideal sellers have ever existed outside economic textbooks, the distinction seems unimportant. However modified, this transactional view still provides the underlying model for all conventional thought.

This transactional view still holds in a state-funded or insurance-funded service. Who pays, and whether payment is by salary, flat rate capitation for continuing care, or by episodic fees for items of service,

has powerful effects on the nature of consultation, by changing motivation in providers and expectations in consumers, but none of these fundamentally change the underlying relationship between provider and consumer, as long as these roles are maintained. Transaction implies *caveat emptor*, let the buyer beware. There is a fundamental conflict of interest between buyer and seller, just as there must also be some fundamental convergence of interest for the transaction to begin in the first place. If patients are consumers, their rights and power can increase only if the rights and power of providers are diminished. Though each clearly needs the other, if understood as providers and consumers, doctors and patients have a fundamentally adversarial relationship.

As soon as we think seriously about this idea, it starts falling apart. If patients are consumers, what do they consume? It's true that patients, not doctors, consume the pills, but it is doctors who choose whether and what to prescribe, and doctors are the target of pharmaceutical advertising for prescribed drugs, not patients. Patients have operations, not their doctors, but doctors decide if an operation is necessary, and what it will be. If consultations simply initiate consumption by patients of something provided by doctors, what and where is the product of medical care? It seems that all transactions as normally understood either precede consultation (pills purchased from pharmaceutical companies for prescription by doctors) or follow it (technical interventions purchased from hospitals through a doctor's referral). What about a consultation in which nothing is prescribed, and no referral is made? Does this have no product? As most health economists now acknowledge, for pharmaceutical companies and Hospital Trusts which are the main market players, GPs are the consumers, not their patients.

Patients as co-producers of health

An alternative and more useful assumption is that both doctors and patients jointly create a product through consultation, which did not previously exist. The primary consultation process may or may not initiate consumption of other products of critical interest to other market players, notably prescribed drugs in about 70% of consultations, and referrals for complex diagnostic tests or technical interventions in about 7%, but these are secondary to the main product of all consultations. This product is understanding of patients' problems, and steps toward their solution, ultimately leading to net health gain.

Though all productive consultations depend, and always have depended, on work by both doctors and patients, doctors established a dominant role, with the patients' contribution so subordinated, that doctors could appear wholly responsible for the final product. The terms of private medical trade required that this be so, for otherwise patients could have negotiated a reduced fee, in proportion to their own work — or even, in some circumstances, a fee from the doctor. The full potential of patients as producers cannot be revealed until fees are long forgotten.

In the 95% of problems apparently solved at primary care level, without referral, the patient's contribution to production is high, because this need not conform to any academically respectable form, and can follow intuitive patterns that include much larger inputs from patients. So far as I know, we have no quantified evidence about this. But for the 7% who are referred for a specialist out-patient opinion, patients' contributions to definition of their problems is much larger in fact (though not in appearance) than the contribution of doctors. Studies of medical out-patient consultations show that 86% of diagnosis depends entirely on what patients say, their own story. What doctors find on examination adds a further 6%; and technical investigations (X-rays, blood tests, etc.) add another 8%[25]. To most lay people and even some doctors, these figures are astonishing, the reverse of the proportions expected. Yet in fact even these understate the degree to which the diagnosis depends on intelligent participation by patients, because both physical examination and technical diagnostic tests are not fixed routines, but chosen according to hypotheses generated by listening to patients' own account of their problems.

As for treatment, it is self-evident that once out of a hospital, patients can and do take their own decisions. Research shows that these are more likely to follow a rational and effective plan if patients know their doctors and nurses, believe in them, and feel they have shared in decisions[26].

Above all, this is true for continuing care of chronic or recurrent problems such as diabetes, high blood pressure, asthma and chronic bronchitis, back pain, arthritis, epilepsy, schizophrenia, severe depression, and virtually every other treatable but essentially incurable problem. As every clinician and health economist knows, these are the conditions where current provision fails, where the greatest scope for improvement exists, and where the greatest savings through prevention can be found, both in health conserved and in NHS costs contained. There is good evidence that for all these chronic or recurrent causes of ill-health, roughly half of all cases are undetected, roughly half those detected are not treated, and in roughly half of those treated, underlying disease processes are not controlled (the Rule of Halves[27]). There is also good evidence that for such patients at high risk of serious acute problems, continuing anticipatory care is much more cost-effective than either indiscriminate health promotion clinics of the sort originally promoted by the 1989 GP contract, or attempts at salvage by crisis interventions[28, 29]. Continuing anticipatory care requires mutual respect between health workers and patients.

Recognition of patients as co-producers rather than consumers would begin to solve several problems which are otherwise likely to get worse. As co-producers, patients must share much more actively both in defining their problems and in devising feasible solutions, than they have in the past. At present, diagnosis in exclusively medical terms, excluding related social problems often more relevant to patients' real concerns, promotes somatization of unhappiness (translation of emotional problems into physical symptoms), often leading to inappropriate, wasteful treatment, incurring unnecessary risks as well as monetary cost. If patients were encouraged to play a more active part in defining the nature of their problems, we could approach these very complex and often intractable problems more honestly, with less labelling as "heartsink patients", less fruitless referral of patients to exclude diseases they don't have (rather than search for the real problems they do have) and less inappropriate surgery. With about one-third of all medical referrals having no evidence of organic disease, the scope for savings is immense.

If patients were recognised as essential partners for health production, we could also begin to undo some of the harm done by the adversarial assumptions of litigation for professional negligence. Defensive medicine, clinical decisions prompted by fear of possible future complaint, is not only extremely costly, but also tends to reduce the real quality of care, mainly by occupying time and other resources for what may be useful for subsequent legal defence. Both health professionals and patients need to understand the uncertainties necessarily surrounding all decisions in human biology, and must learn to work within confidence limits broadly understood by both partners. Ultimate legal sanctions against negligence are certainly necessary, but they would be needed less often if doctors were expected to encourage a more active and responsible role to patients, and consultations were no longer regarded as standardised provider-consumer transactions implying guaranteed outcomes.

For a more cost-effective NHS, patients must change from their traditional role as consumers, to a new role as co-producers. This is a different, socialist way to look at health production in the NHS, as neither a state funded autonomous medical hierarchy nor a market of competing corporations dominated by business-trained executives, but a participative democracy developing creative power at the periphery.

All proposed changes in the NHS should be judged as aids or obstacles to this necessary development.

Conditions for changing patients from consumer to producer roles

Several factors influence progress of this shift of patients from consumer to producer roles. Patients generally believe the main obstacles arise from professional attitudes, and there is plenty of evidence to support them.

Though one would imagine that patients who think slowly or are poorly informed would need longer explanations than patients who think quickly or are well informed, doctors tend to give most time to patients who appear most knowledgeable and articulate[30], and to give more time to fellow-professionals than to less educated patients[31]. Despite longer average consultation times than in any other country, a study of physicians in the USA showed they allowed patients to tell their story for an average 18 seconds before interrupting and diverting them to doctor-based topics[32].

Another major study of NHS GPs showed that none, even with psychoanalytical (Balint) training, showed any real interest in patients' ideas about why they were ill, or made any effort to take these ideas into account when working out plans for treatment[33].

However, this is by no means the whole story. A passive consumer role may be a lot more comfortable for many patients in many circumstances, and they may not in practice always be pleased if doctors admit their own limitations, or the present limits of medical science. Doctors who actively try to get off the pedestal often find patients who want to put them back. Doctors determined to abdicate from infallibility rarely fail to carry most of their patients with them, but there are many exceptions, particularly in the first five years or so.

Instead of judging these attitudes, we need to consider reasons why both doctors and patients so often cling to traditional transactional roles, despite mounting and generally accepted evidence that these impair output in consultation. The most important of these is probably simply the time available for consultation. Consultations can be done more quickly, and more certainly steered to conclusions with apparently clear clinical meaning, if patients are subordinated to a passive role. Instead of giving their own full account of their problems as they see them, they are encouraged only to answer key questions, as in legal cross-examination. The case can be wound up more quickly and tidily if the often inconclusive mess corresponding better to reality is ignored. Just as cross-examination serves the convenience of judges rather than truth or justice, early imposition of medical priorities encourages unjustified somatisation, misuse of technical resources and negative net output; but for the doctor it has the overwhelming merit of getting one patient out in time for the next, and for the patient, comforting illusions of simplicity.

Obviously, very short consultations can rarely do more than meet minimal patient expectations, so more time is necessary to develop anything new. Forced to curtail consultations, doctors do so at the expense of newer options such as listening, advising, explaining, preventing, and searching out opportunities for anticipatory care[34, 35]. This hard-headed view of priorities corresponds with the wishes and beliefs of patients, who welcome a search for needs *after* their elementary wants are satisfied, but not as an alternative to traditional demand-led care[36]. However planners and administrators may imagine otherwise, all primary health workers on the ground must either give first priority to known wants, before searching for imagined needs, or lose the confidence of their patients.

When Britain's first mass primary care system began in 1912, the rich doctors of rich people warned that if doctors were paid by salary or capitation to provide mass medical care for the poor, it would be "perfunctory care, by perfunctory men"[37]. So it was, and in large part still is, in most areas of heavy industry, highest unemployment, highest morbidity, and heaviest medical workload. To get beyond this requires not only new attitudes, but also new resources (above all, of time) to make those attitudes possible. Health theoreticians without practical experience of trying to apply medical science within the constraints of ordinary practice are incapable of seeing this as a primarily material rather than moral problem. Bad conditions make bad health workers, not the other way round.

Potential efficiencies of continuity

Compelled to fit gallons of necessary care into pint-pots of time, NHS GPs took advantage of their one supreme asset, continuity of care. If all you have is about 5 minutes, you learn to remember, or better, to record, a cumulative store of information, so that you don't have to start again from the beginning at every consultation.

In the NHS, virtually everyone is registered with their own GP, who keeps a continuing record of both GP and specialist care. This record follows patients to their new doctor if they move. Though we take this for granted, few other countries have any such arrangement. Where, as in most other West European countries, patients can shop around for their care between competing doctors in a free market, or where patients have direct access to specialists, there is no organised transmission of records between family doctors, no properly organised referral system, and no systematic exchange of information between primary care teams and hospital specialists. Virtually all relevant information may have to be assembled all over again in each episode of illness, and it is simply not possible to build up any continuing story of people's lifetime experience of health care.

Continuity of care — seeing not strangers, but people you already know, and not isolated clinical events, but successive episodes in life stories — is enormously important for real clinical efficiency[38, 39, 40], for patients to make sense of what happens to them, and thus help them to become active producers[41], and so for health gain. This need not mean always seeing the same doctor, since doctors no longer

work 24 hours a day, and continuity should not mean that patients 'belong' to their doctors. It means patients need to be registered with one small team of people who all use, record and share the same information efficiently. This is extremely difficult to achieve with traditional record systems, not only because the rhetoric of teamwork is far in advance of reality, but because of practical difficulties of duplicating written information and retrieving it from thick files. Computerised information systems, so often seen as dehumanising, are in fact a precondition for the personalised, democratised continuing anticipatory care we need, including medical records held by and accessible to patients themselves.

Continuity is not in practice valued in a competitive market, in which consultations are seen as isolated provider-consumer transactions, scattered between competing providers. Free markets depend on shopping around, encouraging short-term consumer choices, impulse buying, salesmanship and promotion of packaged technical interventions to patients as passive consumers of health care, not critical co-producers of health.

Nor can the competitive market, at least as presently constituted, expand consultation time. The greatest cost in the NHS is the cost of labour, so the greatest scope for savings and improved efficiency appears to be replacement of labour by machinery, or saving of labour by speed-up. More people processed in less time may represent greater output efficiency if we are talking about technical interventions, but this is untrue of consultation at any level. Unless consultations are understood as the points of production of critically important decisions which determine all other consumptions, the cost-effectiveness of the entire NHS will fall in terms of net health gain, even if it improves in terms of reduced waiting times or raised output of technical procedures. The quality of consultations must in large part depend on freedom from time pressures, without perverse incentives to save time by ill-considered somatisation, prescription or referral, and with protected time in which to develop patients' capacities as producers rather than consumers.

The overwhelming experience of all NHS staff over many years, is that unless they simply stop trying, they can never stop running. Diagnosis and initiation of treatment on the run is both wasteful and dangerous. If professional staff are rushed off their feet, they cannot listen, inform, explain, or sympathise. All they can do is give orders, and there is no hope at all either of encouraging patients to develop new, more active and responsible roles, or of persuading professionals to help them do so.

Yet this is precisely where current notions of productive efficiency lead us; more output from less labour by fewer people. If doctors are seen as active providers of health care in commodity-units to passive consumers, efficiency will be measured as output of process, not output of health gain. If the consultation is recognised as the birthplace of both good *and* bad care, requiring time to develop the critical imaginations of both patients and professionals as co-producers, we can begin to make the entire system more rational and therefore more cost-effective. Without this, the NHS will just keep on growing, bigger but not better.

7

Primary care: potential wealth, actual poverty

Medical science advances faster than social understanding or structure. Family doctors can in theory do far more for their patients in 1994 than in 1912, but in practice the time available to do it has increased very little, and imagination has been correspondingly constrained. Doctors self-employed as entrepreneurs contracting to provide public service preferred to work alone, rather than spend relatively small earnings on more staff. Most of the new and effective techniques developed by medical science required not only more time, but also a larger and more diverse team than community generalists found it economic to provide. Advances in medical science were therefore mainly applied by hospital specialists, not community generalists.

In this common currency of clinical time, salaried or capitation-paid generalists were too poor to use much medical science, except by hasty prescription of the magic bullets promoted by the pharmaceutical industry. Most GPs still work in clinical poverty, where a free tabloid trade magazine paid for by pharmaceutical advertising (Pulse) has more readers and is regarded by more of them as useful, than the British Medical Journal[42], and MIMS, a prescribing handbook distributed by the pharmaceutical industry, has far more users than the excellently produced and far more authoritative British National Formulary, distributed free by the Department of Health.

Many GPs try to preserve their self-respect by denying this scientific poverty. They deny any need for the academic exactness of teaching hospitals and research centres, boasting that their work is of a more practical, common-sense nature. Patients have common, vulgar diseases, easily subdued by spraying with magic bullets fired from the hip, without pretence of diagnostic accuracy, and still assisted by close human relationships long forgotten in hospitals. These denials deceive nobody. Why endure 8 or 10 years of arduous training, only to end by denying that scientific knowledge is as necessary to solve the most common and important health problems in the community, as it is to solve clinical puzzles in hospitals?

From an appallingly low base in 1948, NHS GPs generally made remarkable progress in quality of care, often with little interest or assistance from their hospital colleagues, and always with indifference from administration, until the NHS market "reforms" set an entirely new agenda. By the late 1960s, NHS GPs began independently to redefine their role. They became more interested in social and personal problems patients actually had, and less satisfied with merely excluding organic diseases they did not have. Family doctors began to accept much wider clinical responsibilities, and became more selective in their referrals to specialists. New outpatients referred by GPs fell steadily from 302/1,000 population in 1962 to 161/1,000 in 1976. This was followed by a slow rise to 186/1,000 by 1986, still 38% below the 1962 level, and down again to 156/1,000 by 1990[43]. This fall in referrals was accompanied by a steep and sustained rise in GP-initiated laboratory and X-ray investigations, confirming that more clinical responsibility was being accepted by family doctors and their primary care teams[44].

However, until much larger investments of time, effort and imagination are put into staff and team development to deal with continuing anticipatory care of chronic or recurrent health disorders, a large gap will remain between the minimum clinical standards expected in hospital out-patient departments, and those customary in general practice. This issue has suddenly become urgent because there is now administrative pressure for redeployment of follow-up care from hospital out-patient clinics to primary care teams.

Diabetes: a model for continuing anticipatory care

A good example of the size and nature of the problem is care of non-insulin dependent diabetes. A study in Cardiff compared patients with this disorder randomly allocated either to follow-up care by their GP, or to continue attending the hospital clinic. The GPs had agreed to this, and to follow a simple management protocol monitoring important health indicators for diabetics, such as urine tests for protein, tests for blood glucose, and examination of the retina. When both groups were followed up 5 years later, all the patients randomised to their family doctors had been seen, usually several times, but only 14% had been monitored annually according to protocol, compared with 100% of hospital patients. Three times as many of the GP patients had died[45]. Similar studies elsewhere have shown similar figures[46, 47].

This difference in quality of care has little to do with the competence of specialists compared with GPs. Most routine follow-up work in hospital diabetic clinics is done by junior medical staff in training, not by specialists, and most of these junior doctors go on to become GPs. The real difference is that hospital doctors inherit traditions of team care, with supporting nurses, laboratory and office staff, all of whom contribute to successful running of a clinic, whereas family doctors inherit a tradition of single-handed practice, from which they have only recently moved toward group practice, and even more recently to employment of full office staff and practice nurses. As independent contractors, family doctors must still fund much of their work from their own incomes, whereas in hospital this is a responsibility for administration. Adequate care of diabetics starts (and all too often ends) with a strict checklist of a few essential measurements. Experience shows that in practice these measurements are simply not done, unless clinics are organised for the specific purpose, and non-attenders are actively followed up. To organise such community-based clinics for the first time requires organising skills and imagination which have only recently begun to be taught or even encouraged in our medical schools.

Yet the results even of hospital diabetic care are generally poor compared with what we know to be possible, and mostly inferior to the best that have been achieved by the most innovative community primary care teams. These have usually evolved from systems of shared care, in which follow-up by primary care teams is integrated with the work of a hospital diabetic department[48]. Diabetic care depends above all on well-informed, well-motivated patients, who understand the nature of diabetes, its complications, and how to avoid them, who measure health indicators such as blood or urine glucose levels themselves, set specific targets and check their attainment[49]. They participate as co-producers of their own health, a gain both for themselves and for the community, which then has fewer people to treat for gangrene, blindness, or kidney failure — a social as well as a private product. Obviously all these tasks are potentially better done in the community, where patients look larger and doctors a bit smaller.

This is just one example of a very general shift in the nature of health care. Traditionally, health services everywhere have given priority to crisis intervention, repairing damage after it occurred. This remains the image of medical care favoured by television drama and most exciting to the public. But we can now see that though repairs, where possible, are obviously necessary, a repair system will work most efficiently if underpinned by a much wider system of continuing health maintenance, which can diminish the need for crisis interventions in the first place, and so far as possible ensure that they do not recur, leading to the "revolving door" system familiar in US emergency departments. For example, a brief anti-smoking programme administered by nurses[50] has been shown to be 500 times more cost-effective, in terms of years of life saved, than coronary bypass graft surgery[51]. Medical science has already developed far enough for us to see real future possibilities of maintaining health in most people continuously, right up to the point where they die a natural and relatively abrupt death[52].

Managed competition

Medical care the world over now stands on the brink of a huge expansion of investment in health care, in two possible directions: either to need-driven co-ordinated expansion of labour-intensive continuing care and health maintenance for whole populations, with episodic technical repair as a subordinate tool; or profit-driven independent expansion of capital-intensive technical repair, as an ultimately false alternative to continuing care, directed mainly at profitable subgroups of the population. These are mutually exclusive; no imaginable society can afford both, and the professional attitudes required are entirely different. Struggle between these two tendencies defines the true crisis in medical care[53].

There are many different views on the future of health services, but on one point everyone agrees; they are everywhere in crisis. With the curious exception of Cuba, there are no developed national systems of health care anywhere that are not now being subjected to fundamental revision.

Why is this so? According to conventional wisdom, the immediate cause is that scientific advance has priced medical care beyond the reasonable costs of public service. The advance of medical science continually expands what is possible, much faster than any government can afford to apply it to all who might benefit. Unless we find some way of reining in medical care, the entire Gross National Product will eventually be consumed by health services. If you really think about it, this is unconvincing. All sciences expand, not just medical science. Has anyone announced a similar crisis in telecommunications, genetic engineering and biosynthesis, or computer games? The problem arises not because of the rapid progress of medical science, but because of the peculiar social relations within which medical science has hitherto been applied. These other rapidly expanding industries, all dependent on science, are extremely profitable, and therefore recognised to generate value. Their rapid growth may cause some problems, but we assume the new wealth they generate will ensure far more gains than losses; they pay for themselves. Public health services are different, precisely to the extent that they are freely available to all, not bought or sold, and therefore not profitable to trade.

Health services create wealth

Obviously, if health services have any positive output in net health gain, they must create value. Most people value their health more highly than any other quality except happiness, so if they believe they need medical care, in a market economy they give it high priority in personal spending. Research has shown clearly that to consumers, spending on personal medical care is a necessity, not a luxury, so that only food commands higher priority in the budgets of poor families[54].

Margaret Thatcher and Joe Stalin shared one philistine assumption. Both of them classed health services in the "non-productive sector" of the economy, like education, cultural institutions, and everything else not producing objects or services for sale. In this view, my lifetime of caring for the health of coal miners and their families in a free public service was an essentially parasitic activity of wealth consumption, not wealth production; whereas if I had performed the same tasks for rich Arabs visiting Harley Street, I would have been an economically useful wealth-creator. Almost the first serious school of economists were the physiocrats of pre-revolutionary France, who believed that all real wealth was created by agriculture, all other value being ultimately derived from it. They were specially contemptuous of manufacturing industry, which in their view merely took agricultural products and manipulated them in various ways, without adding to their essential value. This absurd view was as natural to them, as the non-productive nature of all public service seems today to people who can perceive only lost opportunities for profitable trade.

At least until about ten years ago, market production and distribution of medical care resembling other typical developed commodity markets did not exist. If we take car production as a typical example, a developed commodity market consists of a diminishing number of giant multinational corporations serving world-wide markets, so rich that they often have more control over elected governments, than governments have to control corporations. Medical market economies were not of this nature, because for many different reasons, production of personal health gain was not suited to investment on anything like the same scale.

There were essentially three kinds of medical market. In economically undeveloped countries, medical care was sold by and bought from individual self-employed physicians and surgeons, specialists in cities but general practitioners in the countryside, working alone or with a few supporting staff. Doctors provided their own capital equipment, of which by far the largest component was their own personal investment in training. A few got very rich, but they were an insignificant part of the economy as a whole. In every economically developed country except the USA, though relics of this self-employed private medical shop-keeping remained, most medical care passed to salaried or contracted public medical services, created to humanise otherwise intolerable industrial systems, under pressure from socialist and trade union movements, either as powerful oppositions or in government.

The USA evolved a unique position. Her socialist and trade union movements were too weak to require any comprehensive care system covering the whole population, and medical care was left to be developed by doctors as self-employed entrepreneurs. As medical care came to require capital investment beyond the power of even the richest doctors, they acquired public investment, first from their communities, then from insurance companies, and finally from government, but medical trade remained under professional control.

By the 1980s, in all economically developed countries, health services were a gigantic industry, a rapidly growing and very significant part of the whole economy. Whereas everywhere else public investment went into public service, in the USA public investment subsidised private medical enterprise. This could not last; as self-employed entrepreneurs, US doctors grew too big for their boots and were ripe for take-over. And that's where the world crisis in medical care began.

The medical-industrial complex

The international crisis in medical care was first recognised as important by health economists in the USA, the world's richest country, with the world's most extravagant, wasteful and unjustly distributed medical care system. In a classic paper in 1980, Dr Arnold Relman, editor of the world's oldest medical journal, the New England Journal of Medicine, startled conservative Bostonians by drawing attention to a huge and in his opinion dangerous new force in the US economy, the medical-industrial complex[55]. He estimated its total wealth as roughly twice as much as the US military-industrial complex which frightened General Eisenhower. It was growing faster than any other investment sector, was uniquely resistant to recession, and yielded exceptional rates of profit. A series of subsequent papers documented the irresistible progress of corporate managers, and ignominious retreat of both liberal and conservative professionals[56, 57].

In this new economic formation, doctors neither controlled the productive process nor set its goals. The main players were the main payers; insurance companies, which financed virtually all medical care, corporate employers whose labour costs included insurance for medical care, and an increasing number of corporate employers of health professionals, such as Health Maintenance Organisations. US doctors had organised production to benefit themselves, resulting in large medical incomes and high costs, both directly to patients, and as tax-burdens on both citizens and (horror of horrors) corporate employers, supporting public programmes such as Medicare and Medicaid. US governments, which had for 60 years refused seriously to consider any of many well documented proposals for universal care systems, at last began to show serious interest in reform, not (of course) in a socialised direction, but toward corporate care on the same pattern as other industries.

This entailed defeating the medical profession as an independent sectional interest, so far as possible incorporating it in the new pattern of corporate care by offering an attractive package of high incomes and increased investment in new technology. However, like all other skilled workers eventually sucked into the capitalist system of production, these doctors, however well paid and extravagantly resourced, ceased to control the aims or nature of their work. The Clinton proposals for medical care reform are fundamentally of this nature. Doctors will lose their private control of what has at last had to be recognised as a public service. They will be replaced by powerful managements, with overall control of clinical as well as logistic policy decisions. These managers will not be elected by the people, but represent corporate interests, mainly the insurance companies which financed Clinton's ascent to the presidency[58].

There are none so blind as those who would not see

By the 1980s, despite mounting competition from Germany and Japan, the United States still had the world's wealthiest and most rapidly expanding economy, and therefore its dominant culture. It also had the world's most advanced medical science and technology, and in line with its other world records, the world's most extravagant, unjust, and inefficient medical care system. Politicians responsible for health care systems in other developed countries were in difficulty. Their original reasons for consensus support for various kinds and degrees of socialised medical care had disappeared. Medical care was now real rather than illusory, entailing huge costs and even bigger potential profits if it could become another field of investment for commodity production; and alternative socialist societies, real or imagined, seemed about to disappear from history. Few politicians can afford distant vision. Having educated their voters to see no further than the next wage packet, their rhetoric and interests must become equally short-sighted. They have no time to design their own new societies, they need working models. Where else should they go to foresee their own future, but the United States?

Like Nye Bevan in 1948, most health care planners in 1994 think they have set their doctors' feet on a new path entirely. They are led by Alain Enthoven, the US health economist called in by Margaret Thatcher to advise her on the future of the NHS in 1985[59]. Among the pilgrims to his shrine at Jackson's Hole was health minister Kenneth

Clarke when he was devising the NHS internal market. Health care systems the world over are now being 'reformed' through some or other version of his concept of managed competition in health services[60], including Australia[61, 62], Finland[63], France[64], Germany[65], Israel[66], Italy[67], the Netherlands[68], New Zealand[69, 70], Spain[71, 72], Sweden[73], and all the former communist command economies except Cuba[74]. As for the poverty-stricken countries of the Third World, they have all been compelled by their creditors to abandon even the scanty public care provision they had to the market[75], with such immediately disastrous consequences that even the World Bank, principal author of their misfortunes, has had to admit overkill.[76]

All of these except Sweden have justified their lurch from professional co-operation to professional competition by imminent bankruptcy of their health care systems. This was not possible in Sweden, because health care costs had already been falling for several years[77], so there the justification was just presumed better value for money through competition.

Origins of managed competition

Alain Enthoven, architect of managed competition, started at the Pentagon under the wing of Robert MacNamara, formerly head of the Ford Motor Company. He developed his theory to rationalise the extravagant decisions of US generals in the Vietnam war[78]. Already in 1963 his original mind perceived similarities between organised health care and organised slaughter[79]:

"Beyond its uniqueness and eclecticism, I would like to say that the art of weapons systems analysis, like the art of medicine, should be based on scientific method, using that term in its broadest sense."

These similarities were real. Just as doctors wanted to do whatever science made possible, assuming that health must thereby improve, generals wanted whatever science made possible, assuming their war could thereby be won sooner and at lower cost. Congressmen knew that more money for higher powered medicine was only marginally more popular with voters than more money to help good people kill bad people faster and at lower cost. In both cases, it seemed reasonable to suspect that if strategic decisions could be shifted from self-perpetuating and self-serving professionals, into the hands of more objective, independent managers without personal axes to grind, and if the professionals could be compelled to compete with each other rather than scrub each others' backs, better value for money must follow. The Pentagon agreed, and from 1961 to 1969, Enthoven was in high fashion.

Such was the essence of managed competition: Step 1, bring in new managers from outside the professional military (or medical) field; Step 2, break up the military (or medical) professionals into competing units, rewarding winners and penalising losers on the same lines as any free commercial market; Step 3, base as many management decisions as possible on rational analysis of relevant case-studies, wherever these are available. More cost-effective decisions must follow.

Note that managed competition, as presented by Enthoven, was never intended to reduce or even to restrain overall costs. On the contrary, use of documented case-studies tends if anything to accelerate technical innovation, and the costs of the Vietnam war escalated steeply throughout Enthoven's period of influence at the Pentagon. His claim was merely that all military (or health) dollars, new or old, would be more efficiently and effectively spent.

Note also that Enthoven assumed as fundamental principles that no organisation could work efficiently unless its entire personnel competed on essentially commercial lines, that all organisations eventually used their power to achieve stability by sharing markets rather than competing for them, and that they had then to be compelled to restore competition in the interests of continued growth and innovation.

Enthoven in action

Enthoven's success in commanding the world stage in health care planning is remarkable, not least because his equal eminence in the 1960s as intellectual leader of the Pentagon ended in failure. Application of his principles did not in fact result in the order-of-magnitude improvements in efficiency he had so confidently predicted, which were supposed to justify his infuriation of military professionals subjected to corporate management. Like all failed prophets, his own explanation was that his plans were never fully implemented.

Obviously, Enthoven has a talent for saying what powerful people wish to hear; that failure of a giant economy rich in technology to prevail over a small one already "bombed into the stone age", could only be a failure of the military professionals, not a consequence of a fundamentally wrong political choice in going to war in the first place. In the same way, he now explains the failure of the same giant economy rich in medical science to provide a cost-effective health care system, as a failure of medical professionals running the health market, not a consequence of having a market in health care instead of a tax-based public service. Both possibilities, that the Vietnam war was wrong in every dimension, and that socialised public service may be more cost-effective than any market, were excluded from both his imagination, and the minds of his powerful clients.

This conviction that *laissez-faire* economics is a law of nature rather than a human concept is the source of all Enthoven's errors, but even without this perception, they are obvious to anyone willing to look for them. His claim that his corporate administrators would compel professionals to take decisions "based on scientific method, using that term in its broadest sense" does not survive critical examination. Far from using scientific method in its broadest sense, he in fact misused it in precisely that narrow sense which brings science into disrepute; he continually failed to question or even to recognise his fundamental assumptions, he ignored the wider context of problems, and he used selected case-studies to illustrate and endorse conclusions he had already reached, instead of setting up objective controlled trials in representative areas to test his hypotheses. His aim was not in fact to prosecute a war, or to establish health care systems, on a basis of science, but in both cases to move from what he saw as self-serving intuitive behaviour by military or medical professionals, to more rational and objective decisions by independent business managers.

Though both doctors and soldiers use the products and some of the techniques of science, few are themselves scientists. War is a messy business, and so is clinical medicine. To use a possibly confusing analogy, these are both fields in which "gardening is real, and botany is bogus"[80]. Evidence about what is actually going on is scarce, and the apparent quality of what there is tends to be deceptive; the tidier and less ambiguous it seems, the less likely it is to be in any way representative of what actually happens. In both cases, there is a permanent and potentially fruitful tension between workers in the field, who value experience more than theory, and planners at staff HQ or in the laboratory, who value theory more than empirical experience. "Practice without theory is blind, theory without practice is sterile"; the temptation to ignore either side of this equation must always be resisted, and the true glory of medical professionalism has been its steady progress toward combination of theory and practice in everyday work, from top to bottom of the care system.

Speaking to European health planners and economists at an OECD conference in 1990[81], Enthoven was disarmingly frank:

"What can Europeans learn from Americans about the financing and organisation of medical care? The obvious answer is 'not much'. We Americans are spending nearly 12%, going on 15%, of Gross National Product on health care, while most European countries are spending an apparently stabilised 6 to 9%. The Western European democracies have achieved essentially universal coverage, but some 35 million Americans — 17.5% of the population under 65 years of age — have no financial protection against medical expenses, public or private."

He went on to say that the main lessons Europeans should learn were not from US successes, but from their mistakes, and that what was actually needed was convergence by all national care systems toward his own preferred rational model, managed competition. The only mistake he seemed able to recognise in the USA was not that a competitive market in health care still existed which West European countries had long ago discarded, but that the US medical market was still run by the medical profession in its own interest. Even for Europe, his remedy was essentially the same; end medical autonomy, put corporate managers in charge, and expose all health workers to the full force of market competition.

Margaret Thatcher: let the market rip

When Margaret Thatcher brought her new generation of young Tories to power in 1979, her social programme was simple; limit government to the minimum required to make business secure, let businessmen enrich themselves as much and as quickly as possible, and have faith that the rest would follow. Their hero was Adam Smith, an extremely complex, thoughtful, and humble genius, with a talent for going straight to the heart of things, but wonderfully tempered by doubt. Whether or not she ever bothered to read what he actually wrote, Thatcher would have agreed with his opinion of the social functions of government in 1762:

"Till there be property there can be no government, the very end of which is to secure wealth, and to defend the rich from the poor"

By the time Karl Marx drew attention to the same thing in the 1840s, it was no longer possible for rulers to declare their aims so frankly. Largely because the industrial working class was becoming a major political force in its own right rather than a subordinate mass ally for liberal capitalists, this simple view of the functions of government had to be modified, co-opting some of the objectives of working people, including education, housing, sanitation and health. The overall context remained the same — to secure wealth in its unequal distribution — but the modifying additions had different meanings for workers and for masters. For workers they were an absolute gain, hopefully expanding indefinitely to a more civilised future. For masters they were a burden, justified only by the greater industrial efficiency possible with a more literate and healthier workforce, and by the greater cultural dominance possible if government by the few could appear to care for the many.

By the eve of the First World War, an end to rule by the few seemed not only possible but imminent, so this was a time of rapid growth in social legislation everywhere but the United States, where the threat was still small. It accelerated in 1917, reached USA in the 1929 economic crash (Franklin Roosevelt caught up with Bismarck and Lloyd George in 1935), and enormously increased after 1945, when an ostensibly socialist state was transiently recognised throughout Europe as the main instrument of Hitler's defeat. Welfare states were not only an absolute gain for the mass of the people, but seemed essential to survival of

capitalism as a competing world model of society. Few then doubted that from then on, there would always be another society which capitalism had to be better than.

Margaret Thatcher and her young Tories were among the first to recognise the end of this era. They recognised the internal weakness of socialist states which could get beyond primitive industrialisation only by adopting the market philosophies they had despised, led by Communists who feared their own most powerful ideas; and that the downfall of "actually existing Socialism" would drain out such blood as Democratic Socialist parties elsewhere possessed. Confident she could cope with the opposition, she set out to cut government back to its original primitive functions, to deregulate society, and allow mass unemployment to destroy Trade Union power. Note that Adam Smith said the government's job was to secure wealth, not to augment it. Production was not a task for government, but simply one way of making money for business, which should be left alone to pursue profit by any and every means, from which public good was bound to come. Her vigorous views stemmed directly from Nobel prize-winning Chicago economist Milton Friedmann, who boldly pronounced that:

> "Few trends could so thoroughly undermine the very foundations of our free society as the acceptance by corporate officials of a social responsibility other than to make as much money for their shareholders as possible."[82]

Unfortunately for British manufacturing industry and from three to five million unemployed workers, more profit could be made by being clever with property or other people's money, than by producing anything useful. In the short term, more people appeared to gain than to lose; assisted by selling off national assets and by winning a war too small to lose, Mrs Thatcher won her next election by a thumping majority.

Birth of the NHS "reforms"

Despite Thatcher's zeal for privatisation, and loathing for all things socialist, even she recognised the huge popularity of the NHS, and particularly of its most socialist features — available to all, free at time of need, given according to need not ability to pay, and so on; the social justice bit was what everyone liked best. Up to 1987, despite many suggestions from New Right think tanks for retreat to marketed care, Mrs Thatcher would have none of it. She had promised the NHS would be safe in her hands, so she left it alone. But in 1987 the NHS ran out of money, acute hospital beds began closing on a greater scale than ever before, and individual cases of children denied necessary life-saving surgery reached the headlines. Something had to be done.

Faced by mounting evidence that the NHS was grossly underfunded, under cross-examination by a hard-nosed BBC interviewer, without consulting any of her cabinet colleagues, Mrs Thatcher promised to set up a personal review of the NHS, to find a better method of financing. She set it up, and for the next 12 months it continued to meet in secret. None of its discussions, nor any of the evidence or options it considered, have been published, but they certainly included all the favourite nostrums of the New Right — state-assisted private insurance, voucher schemes, and so on. None of them would, in the opinion of the Treasury, raise money so cheaply and efficiently as taxation. The review therefore failed in its original proclaimed purpose; no better method of financing could be found than from taxes, but the Conservatives were the low-tax Party.

Meanwhile the NHS staggered from one crisis to the next. The BMA estimated that even to keep the NHS running more or less as it was, funding needed to rise by about 50%, from 6% of GNP to about 9%. This would still be far below US levels, but about average for Western Europe.

In 1988 the NHS Review published its conclusions. The problem, it decided, lay not in funding, but the structure of the NHS, which was inherently wasteful. The trouble with the NHS was that it was run inefficiently, by the medical profession and for the medical profession. Its technical interventions, such as kidney dialysis or coronary bypass surgery, were lagging further and further behind the best of US and West European care not because of underfunding, but because doctors and nurses were not really trying. This was bound to be so, because they lacked the spur of competition, the material incentives of success and penalties of failure in the market. This disease could not be cured by throwing money at it (despite or possibly because of their special respect for money, Conservatives seem always to assume it must be thrown, rather than spent prudently). The NHS must be restructured as a managed market.

On all available evidence, the least costly, least inefficient, least irrational, least socially unjust health service in the world was to be remodelled on untested hypotheses generated by experience of the world's most costly, most inefficient, most irrational, and most unjust health service. It is still hard to understand how anyone who knew anything of the NHS either at administrative or clinical level could possibly have believed in this extraordinary idea, but well-educated collaborators were in fact easily found, as soon as word got round about career prospects in apparently permanently Conservatised society. Managed competition suddenly set high value on anyone able to understand health accountancy and balance sheets in clinical terms, and willing to reconcile scientific culture with boardroom barbarism. Those with academic reputations to protect were allowed to express reservations, so long as they conceded the possibility that managed competition might work and deserved a trial.

Though market reforms of the NHS were opposed by 77% of voters in 1990[83], and have become even less popular as they have moved from theory to practice, opposition from opinion-forming media was almost entirely negative. Return to the past was ruled out, and though the commercialised future on offer was deplored, no other future was considered seriously possible. Consumerism, the common philosophy of all received wisdom from Left to Right, stood in apparent opposition to commercial interests, but seemed to concede that only market production and distribution could ensure high quality service. Having accepted managed competition as inevitable in principle, all we had from guardians of the old consensus was agonised hand-wringing over consequences, without serious discussion of alternatives.

Even without a fully developed alternative social programme, Thatcher's ruthless indifference to the social effects of compelling everyone to become either a winner or a loser eventually threatened to make the Conservative Party as unelectable in the 21st century as similar policies did in the 1940s. Thatcher was traded in for Major, in the hope that greed was now sufficiently re-established as prime mover of society, to look after itself. Helped by another small and unlosable war in the Persian Gulf, this confidence was not misplaced; the Party of Greed survived the 1992 general election.

Thatcherism without Thatcher

Since they threw overboard their apparently redundant baggage of social conscience, British Conservatives have adopted the simple faith of their counterparts in the United States: consumer decisions in the market must always prove wiser, in the long run, than decisions by politicians the consumers elect. Leaders may think they know better, but in the end, the best choice is whatever is most profitable, because it suits most consumers in the market. The solution to all social problems is fully to expose them to market forces. Since in the Conservative view society and the market are more or less interchangeable terms (anyone not in the market is outside society), market decisions must be democratic, because they maximise involvement of consumers; everyone has to buy, but each year fewer people bother to vote. Any attempt to limit the natural behaviour of the market must, therefore, be an infringement of freedom and democracy, and all Socialists must by definition be anti-democratic.

Even in the USA, this set of beliefs leads straight into profound contradictions, of which the most politically important is that it drops all pretence that society is led for its own good by a cultured and socially responsible elite, revealing "a gang of intelligent dwarfs who can be hired for anything"[84].

It also contradicts Enthoven's managed competition, which openly admits manipulation of "natural" market behaviour. As virtually all socialists now concede that there must be at least some place for the market in some areas of production and distribution, the critical difference between the Conservative and Labour Parties is evidently not over the existence of markets or whether they need regulation, but in whose interest the regulations will be devised and applied — the few who live by owning, or the many who live by working?

It's all about the distribution of power and social direction of investment and accountability. Certainly, health professionals must be made fully accountable for their work, and in general they now accept this, some gladly and believing it long overdue, others grudgingly. But who should they be accountable to? In a public service, surely to the public, their elected representatives, or both; not to accountants or managers, and certainly not to Conservative Central Office. Doctors and nurses working in the NHS have been made *internally* accountable to management as never before, but the NHS is now losing all *external* accountability to elected government, local or national. Managers of self-governing Trusts are now accountable only to themselves and to safe nominees appointed by the Minister — the supreme example of the QUANGOs originally denounced by Margaret Thatcher, and then multiplied by her as never before. The important meetings of the NHS Policy Board, of health authorities, and of self-governing hospital Trusts, are held in secret without media coverage, and their unelected members are well paid, appointed for conformity to the new corporate ethos, and fired if they depart from it[85].

As they sowed, so do we reap

Thatcher's original simplistic assumptions have been difficult to sustain in the real world, where politicians must still get themselves re-elected. Competition has to mean losers as well as winners. To let the market rip means allowing more and more units to close, despite deep roots in the communities they serve, with corresponding local loyalties and social efficiencies unattainable by any corporate business. Torn between the thrift of the co-operative public service they reject, and the spiralling inefficiencies of the competitive market they revere, the government has now lost all sense of direction, staggering from one crisis to the next, counting on its new army of NHS public relations officers to turn stink into fragrance.

Take for example Guy's Hospital, flagship of the first wave of self-governing Trusts[2]. Despite opposition by a nine-to-one vote of all staff[86] and a majority of consultants and local GPs[87], its appointed management committee was cajoled into applying for Trust status in 1991. By the end of its first quarter, the Trust had overspent by £555,000. After four months in post, the finance director left his job with a reported severance package of £200,000 plus a BMW car, and continued payment of his annual salary of £70,000 until the end of his 3-year contract[88], while the Trust considered an unforeseen debt of £6.8 million and imposed 400 job cuts[89]. In 1993, Conservative ex-Minister of Health Barney Hayhoe was brought in as Chairman of the now merged Guy's and St.Thomas's Trust[90]. Finally, in February 1994, the Secretary of State Virginia Bottomley announced to the House of Commons that the flagship was scuttled. All its acute facilities would close, moving to St.Thomas' Hospital. Guy's would "become a high quality health and academic campus, serving local patients' needs; training tomorrow's doctors, dentists, and nurses; and exploring the boundaries of medicine"[91]. She was confident none of the charities now paying for the third and final phase of a £140 million treatment and research centre at Guy's would want their money back. One week later £30 million of the £44 million promised by charities had been withdrawn, leaving a £96 million bill for the taxpayer for what Dr Robert

Knight, chairman of Guy's medical committee, described as "the NHS's most prestigious white elephant"[92].

Apologists for the "reforms" concentrate on their proclaimed good intentions, merely to get better value for money, both for patients and taxpayers. No one, not even this government, disputes that the NHS is the cheapest of all national care systems, or that in the past decade, mostly before reform, the average cost of treating in-patients and day-care patients fell by 31%[93], but to the most ardent "reformers" this only indicates how much more might be saved if they really bared their teeth. Appointed to curb professional autonomy, Eric Caines, Chief Personnel Officer for the NHS, declared war on the medical and nursing professions, their power to dictate the pace and direction of clinical policy, and to obstruct changes he considered essential to improve efficiency. The reforms ended all national agreements on pay and conditions with the NHS unions and professional organisations. Local pay flexibility, said Caines, would be his "weapon for breaking 40 years of habit and tradition and seeing how far back we can push all the boundaries". He did "not expect to get results until the present system begins to come apart". This seems to have frightened his friends even more than his enemies[94]. In 1993 he resigned, to teach the next generation of NHS administrators as a professor of health service management, claiming the only reason Health Minister Virginia Bottomley was unable to stem the "lemming-like rush by all and sundry, particularly the BMA and the Labour Party, to condemn the NHS reforms" was "her instinct to douse rather than stoke up conflagrations, [preventing] her from pressing her arguments to their conclusions and demonstrating the will to carry these conclusions through into action"[95]. Were it not for political cowardice, he claimed, at least 20% of NHS staff, 200,000 people, could be sacked without any adverse effect on patient care[96].

Shadow Secretary for Health David Blunkett put his finger exactly on what is happening to the "reformed" NHS, at an MPU/SHA conference in 1993[97]:

"The truth is, the Tories do not know where they are going on any of their health service changes ... The health service was effectively hi-jacked by those who have an interest in ever-greater investment in technology rather than basic measures ... Virginia Bottomley is only the good news queen and [does] not take any responsibility for the activities of the NHS on the ground. Already we cannot get questions answered in the House about Trusts and

GP fundholding practices, because they are responsible for their own activity"

The great illusion: more cure means less care

All these ugly developments are obvious consequences of remodelling the NHS in the image of industrial commodity production for profit. Though this is certainly unpopular, it may still appear acceptable if it seems to assure a larger gross product. Few but the very rich regard Capitalism as a beautiful or even pleasant society, but as an efficient generator of material wealth it has not yet faced a serious competitor.

This assurance of material advance, sufficient to outweigh the spiritual losses it entails, is why though all opinion polls show a large and growing majority, of every voting persuasion, against any sort of commercialisation of the NHS, the market "reforms" have so far been tolerated by enough people to get Conservative governments re-elected. Though there is no evidence yet that the new NHS produces more or better clinical interventions at lower cost than the old NHS, most academic NHS-watchers, Public Health physicians, and health economists seem either to believe it may eventually do so, or that their careers might suffer if they did not pretend so to believe[98]. Few British health economists seem able to endorse Galbraith's forthright statement that economics cannot stand as a value-free socially neutral science, and will remain fundamentally dishonest until it returns to its original designation as political economy[99].

Their hopes stay afloat chiefly because of recent developments in surgical and medical treatment, which seem specially well suited to mass production using industrial techniques. About three quarters of all NHS costs are for labour. Industrialised care, replacing a large, broadly-skilled medical and nursing workforce by a much smaller force of specialised technicians, might greatly reduce NHS costs while at the same time giving a much larger output of apparently effective clinical interventions. If this trend toward technological cures could be combined with withdrawal of the NHS from continuing responsibility for people needing labour-intensive care rather than repair, Mrs Thatcher's original problem of ever-increasing NHS costs might be partially solved.

Abdication from continuing care

The second part of this strategy is already in place. The NHS is withdrawing from the largest areas of continuing care. In 1994, there are three-quarters of a million people over 85, most of whom are unable to live independently. By the year 2000 this will reach one million, and by 2020, 1.3 million — an 80% rise over the next 30 years. These projections were known in the early 1980s, when the then government Chief Medical Officer warned that between 1980 and 2000, the number of people aged 85+ would double. As per-capita NHS costs for this age group were nine times more than for people of working age, the NHS faced a truly colossal impending burden of care for which it was in no way prepared[100]. The Conservative response to this has not been to increase provision, but to transfer responsibility so far as possible from the NHS, where it was free and funded from taxation, to carers at home and to local government, where it was funded by patients and families, assisted by means-tested social security payments, and where shortfalls could be blamed on local government. Between 1990 and 1992, 35,000 geriatric hospital beds were closed. Over the same period 9,000 more day-care places, over 45,000 more residential community care places, and some improved home services were added, all from local government budgets supplemented by Social Security, so that public subsidies for community care rose from £10m to £1,700m a year[101]. Local authority budgets are compelled by law to spend 85% of their community care budgets in the private sector. Step by step, Conservative governments have withdrawn care of the elderly and chronic sick from the scope of NHS responsibility[102].

Nobody wants to die in a thinly-disguised workhouse smelling of stale urine and disinfectant, a fair description of most of the "chronic" care available from local authorities under Part 3 of the National Assistance Act well into the 1970s, the "Golden Age" of the NHS. Care for the chronic sick, disabled, and elderly within the community, and if possible in their own homes, is what all of us want for ourselves and for society as a whole. But from bitter experience of high promise but poor delivery in shifting care of mental illness from hospitals to community, we are rightly suspicious of similar proposals for community care of other chronic disorders requiring more care than cure. After all, why were hospitals invented in the first place? Because care of equivalent standard was far cheaper in hospital than at home.

As we all know, and even this government admits, its principal aim is to save money, and wherever it has to be spent, to make sure it reaches the pockets of entrepreneurs. We are therefore bound to suspect that the community care that will replace hospital care will either be of a much lower standard, or increasingly funded by patients and their families.

This government is embarked on a grand strategy of shifting NHS resources so far as possible away from continuing care, toward exclusive responsibility for episodic cure; to fixing what can be fixed quickly and at reasonable cost by doctors with nursing support, but abandoning responsibility for continuing care by nurses with medical support. According to the Department of Health, it no longer bothers to collect central data on the number of continuing care beds in the NHS, but in 1993 the *Guardian* obtained its own data from two NHS health regions and found that 40% of such beds had been closed since 1988. Another study by the Alzheimer's Disease Society found that 56% of a sample of 48 NHS health districts nationally had cut such beds between 1990 and 1993, with an average reduction of 35%[103].

Anyone who doubts that any government would dare to do this without an election mandate should consider the contest in February 1994 between Leeds Health Authority and the NHS Ombudsman, William Reid[104]. In 1990 a 55-year old man was admitted to hospital with a severe stroke, leaving him incontinent of urine and faeces, unable to communicate, walk, or feed himself. The hospital discharged him to a private nursing home in 1991, on the grounds that it had done all that was possible to cure him, and had no continuing obligation to care for him. Like most other health authorities, Leeds HA no longer had any long-stay beds, nor had it any contract with private nursing homes to provide them. His family had to meet the difference between social security benefits and the cost of the private nursing home, which came to £6,000 a year.

The Ombudsman found in favour of the patient and his relatives, and ordered Leeds HA to meet all past and future costs of care. After a similar case two years ago against Cambridge HA, in which the Ombudsman also found in favour of the patient, the then Minister refused to revise guidelines for chronic care, so hospitals continued to close long-stay beds. This time junior Health Minister Baroness Cumberledge had to admit that "There is a clear obligation on health authorities to pay for continuing health care of seriously ill patients", an admission which Philip Hunt, director of the National Association of Health Authorities and Trusts, described as having "absolutely enormous" cost implications for the NHS. Note that this momentous decision to reaffirm what virtually everyone must have assumed was the traditional responsibility of the NHS ever since 1948, and which no Party ever dared openly to question or test at the polls, depended on the continued independence and integrity of just one man, the NHS Ombudsman. The Leeds and Cambridge HAs were pursuing government policy so far as they could, and will no doubt do so again if the Minister can find some way round this ruling.*

* According to the *Independent* (13.8.94); the government has formally marked the end of the "cradle to the grave" NHS by abandoning a national guarantee that elderly patients needing long-term care cannot be placed in private nursing homes against their wishes. Instead under draft guidance, HAs will draw up their own local definitions of who is entitled to continuing NHS care.

Who cares?

Informal carers at home have always provided the default backup for inadequate and often inhuman public service, which in the pre-NHS days of the Poor Law was frankly designed to be more unpleasant than home care (the 19th century workhouse Doctrine of Less Eligibility). People my age remember when elderly married couples, forced to accept workhouse accommodation segregated by sex, were allowed to visit each other only at fixed times, and had no privacy or personal possessions beyond what could be kept in a bedside locker. A huge majority of people still live independently as long as they can, dreading entry to any institution. Despite a large increase in the elderly population throughout the 20th century, growing institutionalisation is a myth. In 1906, 6% of the population over 65 were living in Poor Law institutions. By 1990, only 5% of an older over-65 population lived in geriatric homes, hospitals and psychiatric units[105].

Ungrateful children and uncaring relatives and neighbours are also largely mythical. Since some people hate each other, often with good cause, and many are childless, universal voluntary support for aged relatives will never be possible, but there is no good evidence of substantial evasion of responsibility by families[106], and plenty of evidence that most accept heavy burdens over many years, often with little professional support. Typically, a 1981 community study[107] of 1,066 people over 70 found that 32% needed regular help. Of these more or less dependent people, 11% were in residential accommodation, public or private, 8% were cared for at home by NHS or local authority social service departments without help from relatives, and 2% were unable to name any main carer. The other 79% were cared for by spouses, relatives, friends or neighbours. Of these main carers, 79% were women, and 19% were themselves over 75, often in poor health. Less than half had had a break from caring for even a few days during the previous year, and those with the heaviest burdens of care were least likely to have had such a respite. Another study of community care of dementia found that of an estimated 80,000 sufferers in Scotland, only 10% got any specialist help and less than 19% even benefited from the home help service. Informal care provided by relatives in Scotland for dementia patients was estimated to save the government about £1.2 bn annually[108].

These are still the typical contexts within which caseload shifts from long-term hospital to community care must operate, and against which the new Community Care Act should be judged. One year after its introduction, a major survey found that more than one in four people caring for an elderly or disabled relative or friend had not heard of the new community care system, almost three in four said the people they cared for had not yet had their needs assessed, and less than one in seven thought community care had brought any improvement[109]. In practice, the Act has in large part shifted the costs of terminal care in old age from the tax-funded NHS to personal savings of the elderly themselves. As the only major asset possessed by most old people is their home, John Major's proclaimed vision of "wealth cascading through the generations" seems more likely to be realised as wealth cascading into the new homes-for-the-aged industry, from people who paid a lifetime of taxes for the NHS[110].

Surgical conveyor belts

The only plausible excuse for not caring is curing. Suitably presented as affordable only if families pay for their own continuing care outside the NHS, exciting advances in cure might persuade enough voters to bargain away the rights of all citizens to care almost all of them will one day need, in return for immediate access to cures which most will never need. Just such advances are now on offer.

Quick-fix, mass-produced episodic repairs are now the most rapidly growing part of medical care. Obvious examples are many forms of day surgery, endoscopic "keyhole" surgery, prosthetic replacements (for example, plastic hip joints), organ transplants, and developments in medical treatment that replace common surgical procedures (for example, H2 antagonists replacing partial gastrectomy for duodenal ulcer). Though some of these are already familiar, the scale of imminent change is still not generally understood.

Cholecystectomy (removal of the gallbladder, usually for gallstones) is a common and typical example of these changes. In the 1950s this operation normally required about two weeks in hospital and another four weeks of convalescence at home. Because of better surgery resulting in less tissue damage, and changed attitudes to early mobilisation, by 1985 this fell to 9.9 days[111]. Endoscopic surgery now promises to reduce this even further, with more than half of all patients leaving hospital within 24 hours and the rest within three days[112]. This is a huge increase in productivity. It should release resources for other purposes, and is an obvious argument for the industrial model. Though this procedure only began in France in 1988, by 1992 60% of UK cholecystectomies were performed endoscopically[113], and the first robotic cholecystectomy has now been reported from Canada[114].

Already by 1987, more than half of all surgery in the USA was being done without an overnight stay in hospital, compared with about 20% in Europe[115]. Experts predict that within two years 95% of all elective abdominal surgery in the USA will be performed endoscopically, and that in the UK by the year 2000, open surgery will be as unusual for all standard elective operations as endoscopic surgery seems today[116].

Hospital beds per 1,000 population have been falling almost since the beginning of the NHS, because of improved health and declining chronic disease, and because of gains in efficiency through integrated planning. The fall accelerated throughout the Thatcher and post-Thatcher years, reaching a total of 120,000 closed NHS hospital beds in the period 1981-93, 34% of the 1981 total[117]. Before deciding that we are about to face a large surplus of hospital beds, replacing the chronic shortage all family doctors have experienced as far back as anyone can remember, we should consider some less obvious effects of facilitating mass-produced surgery on industrial lines. Health economists agree that apart from demographic change, the two main determinants of growth in health care costs are the rate of health care inflation (the difference between rates of increase for health care prices and all prices) and the rate of growth of medical interventions per person[118].

In 1987, the first of these rates was 220% higher in the USA than in the UK, and the second was 21% higher[119]. Much of the difference in health care inflation can be attributed to rapid development of endoscopic surgery in the USA. Though endoscopic surgery reduces labour and hotel costs, it also entails huge investments in technology and training. With operative mortality for open cholecystectomy already reduced to 0.17% at all ages in the best centres[120] there is little scope for further improvement in safety. The only substantial gains for patients will be less discomfort and shorter hospital stay. These are important, but few patients would accept these advantages at the known cost of losing access to other less technical but more supportive parts of traditional care, which most are sure to need if they achieve a full lifespan. Though surgical risks are likely eventually to fall with endoscopic surgery, this has yet to be demonstrated for routine work. In New York State, since laparoscopic cholecystectomy was introduced in 1988, the complication rate for endoscopic surgery was fifteen times higher than for open surgery[121]. Later studies have shown better results, as surgeons become more proficient in the new techniques, but this has a high investment cost in further training, and could entail other costs through loss of older, more flexible skills in open surgery. As late as 1993, review of evidence on endoscopic cholecystectomy had to conclude that it cost a lot more and had as yet been applied to a younger cohort of patients than open surgery[122], hardly a secure base for bold future planning.

More worrying is evidence from the same study that after endoscopic surgery was introduced, the number of cholecystectomy operations in New York State rose by 21%. High capital investment in equipment and training requires intensive use to secure an economic return, creating perverse incentives to overuse technical procedures. As we saw in Table 2, fee-paid care systems already encourage high rates for all elective surgery, with cholecystectomy rates 2.6 times higher in the USA than they are in the UK, though prevalence of gallstones is lower in USA[123]. With the NHS now managed chiefly to streamline output of technical interventions rather than improve less readily measurable all-round care, we are likely to shift toward the same irrational path.

Though endoscopic cholecystectomy may allow gallstones to be removed more efficiently, it ignores and diverts attention from three more fundamental questions: when do gallstones really need to be removed, why do they occur, and can they be prevented[124]? By the end of their lives, roughly 12% of men and 24% of women in the general population have gallstones[125], but over a period of 15 years following detection, only about 18% of these stones get into the bile duct, cause jaundice, severe pain, and require operation[126]. On average, people with gallstones live as long as people without them. Once into the bile duct, gallstones become a major and readily treatable cause of severe pain, illness and death, but cholecystectomy as a preventive measure, at least as an open operation, gives no net health gain to the patient[127]. A host of other abdominal symptoms attributed in the past to gallstones, and therefore thought to justify cholecystectomy, are just as common in people without gallstones[128], and are not helped by operation.

Like most other elective surgical procedures, cholecystectomy is very much a matter for professional discretion, with roughly 2.5-fold differences between individual surgeons and between different localities[129]. Britain (before NHS 'reform') seems to be the only country so far studied in which local cholecystectomy rates correlate rationally with local prevalence of gallstones[130]. Whether this rational practice would survive in an era when hospitals compete for customers seems doubtful.

PART THREE: THE FUTURE

10

Professional accountability: who to, what for?

Enthoven, and other believers in managed competition, freely admit that economic pressures in the doctor-dominated US medical market were inflationary, and encouraged profitable but irrational procedures. However, they claim that if medical autonomy were replaced by managerial autonomy, these would become a thing of the past. Though all the more or less socialised health care systems have more or less successfully contained clinical extravagance by overall curbs on funding, none has yet tried to interfere directly in clinical decision-making by imposing fixed clinical management protocols. Yet this is precisely what has happened to US doctors under managed competition, mainly through the Diagnosis-Related Group system for hospital funding. Paradoxically, this has brought US doctors, the fiercest opponents of state systems and defenders of professional autonomy, under the strictest managerial control. Few informed observers seem convinced that this has in fact controlled US health care costs[131].

We should also consider the possibly serious price we might pay in impaired professional morale, motivation, and imagination, if medical care continues to fragment into competing rather than co-operating ultra-specialties, based wholly on technology, and if the work of doctors and nurses is made to converge toward the soul-destroying "efficiencies" of commodity production. While there may well be short-term gains from maximised specialism and streamlined throughput, we delete the human face and wider imagination of medicine at our peril. The new endoscopists need never see patients' faces at all, only their insides through a tube, projected to a closed-circuit television screen. Even in its present state, the huge majority of health workers and professionals of all grades are still chiefly motivated by a wish to do their work well, because it concerns the lives and happiness of human beings, and is not just a way of earning a living. It may be difficult to preserve, let alone develop motivation of this kind, if doctors relate to machines more than to people.

The industrialisation of care, whether by rationalising ward cleaning or by turning a broadly trained clinician into a conveyor-belt technician, will always be dangerous, but within a co-operative public service these effects might be minimised by all sorts of "uneconomic" measures to bring the fragments back together, to restore some sense of a shared human activity. It is entirely possible that in the not too distant future, many technical operative procedures in otherwise healthy people, such as repair of hernias or surgery for varicose veins, could with advantage be handed over entirely to technicians; but for such development to proceed safely, and without damage to overall staff morale, it must be planned with full regard to its entire social context, not as an opportunity to beat the competition.

Disappearing District General Hospitals

In 1993 these two trends, withdrawal from continuing care and industrialisation of episodic cure or repair, were brought together in one logical conclusion. The district general hospital (DGH) as we have known it, hitherto the main centre of both clinical activity and cost in the NHS, could disappear. In an important discussion document[132], the National Association of Health Authorities and Trusts suggested that most DGH functions could in the near future move either more centrally, to larger and more excellent hospitals able to provide the highest standards of combined specialism, or peripherally, to primary care teams making optimal use of their clinical skills in a better-resourced community setting.

Like earlier plans to close large mental hospitals, transferring a few difficult cases to smaller specialist units but most to community care, the overall strategy makes sense. Much evidence confirms that once their caseload has been accurately defined (a difficult task, not yet fully performed by primary care) general physicians and general surgeons do their work less efficiently (with higher dropout and higher mortality) than subspecialty physicians and surgeons at more central units, serving populations large enough to yield sufficient rare cases to develop and maintain expertise. Very roughly, the average DGH serves a catchment of about 250,000 people. Subspecialty (tertiary care) hospitals serve at least one to five million.

Once we have good primary generalist teams working well in all communities, much relatively simple work now done in hospitals (notably, most follow-up clinics for common chronic conditions such as high blood pressure, diabetes, asthma, epilepsy or psoriasis, and certainly most continuing care for the chronic sick, disabled and elderly) could be done better at primary care level, if primary care teams were fully integrated, staffed, housed, equipped and organised for the task.

Taken together, these two developments appear to remove most of the more obvious current functions of a DGH. There remains a continuing need for local facilities to provide 24-hour skilled medical and nursing cover for serious acute illness, beyond the scope of family doctors mainly because they do not see enough cases to maintain expertise, and because they require high quality laboratory and X-ray department backup which cannot be provided economically in the community.

The new breed of NHS executives has an astonishing capacity to ignore clear evidence that this need will not only persist, but is still growing and has never been fully met. For example, the Greater Glasgow Health Board planned a reduction of 29% in acute beds by 2001, though Matthew Dunnigan, a consultant physician at Stobhill Hospital, had shown that demand for medical beds (measured by deaths and discharges) had risen by 32% from 1980 to 1991[133].

Moves away from the DGH concept also ignore the leadership function for hospital specialists such as diabetologists, cardiologists, paediatricians and neurologists, seen for example in some schemes already established for shared care of diabetes[134, 135] and high blood pressure[136]. Such integrated schemes would be essential for any serious plans to shift continuing care of chronic disorders to primary care on a large scale. Given a major reorientation by specialists in their attitudes to primary care (of which there is already good evidence in a progressive minority of consultants), and big investments in primary care team development, this could be developed very effectively from the traditional DGH base, but an already difficult task would be made almost impossible if these specialists were further centralised.

Though there has been much talk of community hospitals on essentially the same lines as the old cottage hospitals, where family doctors could supervise nursing care of simple though often serious illness, it is not at all clear that this has been fully thought through by anyone. Few family doctors actually want this responsibility, particularly when they realise there will be no resident medical staff and they must cover night emergencies. There is real danger that unless family doctors are encouraged to do community hospital work by fees, they won't do enough, and that if they are so encouraged, they may undertake work beyond their competence. Few urban districts are far from existing DGHs, so community hospitals would not be much more accessible. Nor, if they are properly staffed and equipped, would they be much cheaper; after all, the excuse for closing cottage hospitals everywhere in the 1960s was that they were uneconomic to run.

This is not the first time that the economics of medical care have been revolutionised by technical advance. Since the second world war we have lived through at least three comparable revolutions in hospital care; elimination of tuberculosis, elimination of fevers and poliomyelitis, and control of psychotic mental illness. In every case there were huge savings, but redeployment of these savings to other parts of the NHS was never simple, overall expansion of the NHS always continued, and local hospitals on DGH lines remained its most important planning unit. In future even more than in the past, DGH design will need to be flexible, modular, and adaptable to a very wide range of as yet unforeseeable future developments in care, but to suggest that some kind of locally accessible centre will not still need to exist for populations of 100,000-300,000 is socially irresponsible.

As transfer of care for mental illness from hospitals to community has shown, strategies for shifting institutional care to the community will always require extremely critical scrutiny. Little though we like what we have, without cast-iron guarantees of adequate resourcing, in a period of general retreat it is likely to be better than any alternative on offer, however imaginative. More than any administrator, experienced health workers know how costly it would actually be to transfer care of current hospital standards into the community, though few want to endanger funding of general practice by saying so. There is some published experience of primary care teams which have actually done work of this kind over many years, measuring both inputs and outputs of a systematic shift to continuing anticipatory care in the community and away from episodic hospital referrals. Their clear conclusion is that though change of this sort is possible, necessary, and very effective, it requires a much larger and more diverse staff, complete reorientation of all professionals (and eventually of patients), much more consultation time, a major programme of postgraduate in-service continuing education in protected time, and new approaches to medical records, teaching and research[137, 138].

Few health economists have enough experience of or respect for the daily work of primary care to understand the scale or nature of the changes required. As for administrators, NHS experience now seems almost to disqualify applicants; when the "reforms" hit the NHS in 1990, almost half of all family practitioner committee (now FHSA) administrators were sacked, and almost half the new appointees came from outside the NHS, nearly all from industry or the armed forces[139].

Our own way out of the mess

The NHS "reforms", a mixture of Thatcherite fundamentalism and Majorite opportunism, are an obvious mess, and many people who voted Conservative in 1992 are now ashamed of themselves. Only a Labour government can provide the collective and co-operative philosophy necessary to get us out of it, and resume progressive development of the NHS as a public service rather than a business opportunity.

It is difficult for people immediately responsible for patient care to avoid being swept into grudging acceptance of the new era of managed competition, particularly when they get little help from most of their professional leaders. One by one, most have accommodated to what seems to them more or less permanent Conservative rule. There

is a very general feeling that though the NHS has been badly damaged by managed competition, some good things have come out of it; that though a new government, less obsessed by the market and more willing simply to try things out and see if they work, would be welcome, the thought of yet another root-and-branch reorganisation of the NHS might be the last straw.

In reforming the "reforms", many will expect a Labour government to retain the good bits and discard the bad ones, but so far as possible retain the overall structure much as it has now become. Some of the more brutal executives would probably go, but few will want any witch-hunt of collaborators corresponding to the purge of progressives throughout the years of Conservative rule. In *Health 2000*[140], the Labour Party is already committed to "three key areas which must be addressed", and presumably opposed:

(i) The fragmentation of the funding, planning and prioritising of health care and equal access to the service, through the creation of GP fundholding.

(ii) The development of a commercialised and competitive internal market, based on a contract system designed to replace a co-ordinated and planned approach.

(iii) The operation of a purchaser-provider split in a manner designed to facilitate (i) and (ii) above.

Though much of *Health 2000* provides good material for discussion, it evades any serious discussion of local democratic control, either through existing local government or other elected agencies, and discussion of the purchaser-provider split is unclear.

General Practitioner fundholding

As Health 2000 points out, GP-fundholding is the most immediate and urgent threat to the NHS as an integrated public service, more so even than Hospital Trusts. Even under the internal market, it takes time to shift large organisations from traditions of public service to corporate competition, but the small population units of general practice are more manoeuvrable and have therefore been effective agents of rapid change (a point we should bear in mind when Labour gets the driving seat).

The comprehensive BMA survey of GPs in 1992[141] showed that 10% supported fundholding and 76% opposed it when it was first introduced the previous year. After another year's experience of lavish financial assistance to fundholders and hard times for GPs who stayed out, support rose to 20%, and opposition fell to 62%. It is difficult to know how much of support or opposition was principled, and how much was adaptation to perceived necessity; arrangements for fundholders were generous, and some practices were unable to keep large teams together in any other way. Even among first-wave fundholders, 13% said they currently opposed the whole idea of fundholding, although they felt forced to accept it in order to maintain standards of care. Among second and third wave fundholders, the proportions opposed rose to 18% and 40% respectively.

The effect of all free market competition is to reward success and penalise failure. This is the opposite strategy from a unified public service, in which success normally looks after itself, but failure attracts constructive criticism and support. This did not happen in NHS general practice, precisely because it was *not* a unified public service, but relied on independent contractors. The declared strategy behind fundholding is to push all general practice forward by subsidising competition from the "best" practices as currently perceived. Inevitably, these "best" practices are mostly to be found where workloads are lowest, morbidity and workload are least, net earnings are highest, and recruitment of well-trained staff is easiest[142]; in fact just those nice areas with nice people, most sought after by young doctors looking for comfortable work and high incomes.

Once hospitals have met their contracted targets for clinical activity, further work is not funded, and can be found only from fund-holding practices. Months before the end of the 1993 financial year, hospitals all over Britain had to stop further admissions from non-fundholding practices. By December 1993, surveys by both the BMA and the Labour Party confirmed that two out of five hospitals were giving preferential admission to the patients of fundholding practices. A two-tier service is a present reality, an obvious and intended consequence of the fundholding strategy which none of its supporters can credibly deplore.

In the biblical spirit to be expected from Conservative government, to them that have is given, and (because all GP earnings come from a closed budget) from those that have not, even that which they have is taken away. In 1991-2 the Labour Party surveyed 90 FHSAs[143], getting replies from 69. There were nearly 300 fundholding practices, of which about 30 had set themselves up as trading companies, making profits up to £100,000. Each fundholding practice spent an average of £12,500 buying care in the private sector, and got £20,000 to spend on computers, four times as much as non-fundholding practices. By 1993, there were about 600 fundholding practices, the average allowance for administrative costs for each was £32,500, compared with £1,600 for non-fundholders[144], and all fundholding GPs together controlled £1.8 bn of hospital costs annually[145].

In its discussion paper Health 2000 and in many other public statements, the Labour Party has already committed itself clearly to elimination of fundholding practice if it wins power, and few socialists are likely to disagree.

Locality or area commissioning

We are fortunate that the beginnings of an alternative to fundholding have already evolved naturally from the initiatives of increasing numbers of progressive FHSA administrators and non-fundholding GPs now taking part in locality or area commissioning[146, 147]. Consortia of non-fundholding GPs and FHSAs in more than 60 localities are already known to be negotiating contracts with hospitals in this way, and before the next general election, there will be many more. From such experience, the Labour Party should be able to devise less adversarial ways of connecting hospital provision with local needs.

Fundholding practices are not only likely to pursue their own short-term advantages at the expense of other NHS users, but have small practice populations, rarely over 20,000, and sometimes as low as 7,000. Experience everywhere shows that efficient planning for health care requires minimum populations of 50-100,000. This is because even the commoner technical procedures, such as coronary bypass grafts or hip replacements, occur at very low rates in small populations, making budget forecasts extremely inaccurate. Area or locality commissioning, on the other hand, can normally include well over 100,000 people, and can use the real skills of FHSA planners and community physicians, not just the supposed skills of GPs acting as amateur businessmen.

The essence of this need not be a purchaser-provider split, but simply recognition of the growing division of labour between community-based generalists and hospital-based specialists in our health service ever since Lloyd George. Much though this has been deplored by US observers convinced that hospital specialism is the only possible leading edge for medical science[148], until British GPs were effectively excluded from hospital work, there was no possibility of developing the skills necessary for community-based primary generalists, the most important single achievement of British medicine since the Second World War[149]. Primary care should be growing in the opposite direction, toward the community, not back to the hospital. Primary generalists need to learn to accept more help from other, non-medical health professionals, and from patients themselves. As we have seen, new personal relationships between health professionals and patients as co-producers need to be developed through more imaginative and generous styles of consultation. The practical way to do this is through locality or area commissioning, so that functions performed at any level, in the community or in hospitals, are properly resourced.

11

Purchasers, providers, and the future of clinical autonomy

Whereas GP-fundholding has been divisive, and even now is actively supported only by a minority, the purchaser-provider split has been generally popular with family doctors, and with good reason. In many areas GPs find that for the first time since 1948 hospital specialists show some interest in consumer opinions about the service provided.[150] Specialists providing a rotten service at last provoke real concern and eventual action from NHS administration. Adequately staffed and resourced for the first time, FHSA administrators who long wanted to do more than simply calculate pay for GPs[151], can now show some active interest in the work of primary care teams. Operating in some areas through locality commissioning which can include all GPs not just fundholders, the purchaser-provider split has appeared to create favourable opportunities for co-operation between primary care teams and FHSAs, and a more equal dialogue with traditionally dominant hospital specialists.

These healthy developments have all followed the purchaser-provider split, and some, though not all, are probably caused by the new economic dependence of hospitals on GP referral. However, looked at more carefully, the positive elements in this change need not necessarily depend on a purchaser-provider split and might have been obtained better in other ways. Elected representatives of family doctors and other primary care workers could always have been included in all hospital management committees, and been encouraged by the Department of Health to argue for their needs, based on evidence from clinical audit. FHSAs could always have been properly staffed by imaginative and well trained administrators, including people with community medicine skills, and providing networked information technology to catchment area practices. We didn't have these things for two reasons: because governments believed stagnation in primary care was cheap, and believed all innovation must originate from hospitals; and because most GPs wanted to remain independent contractors, advancing at their own preferred speed, and generally failed to recognise any need for area planning. Both these obstacles steadily diminished throughout the 1970s and 1980s, and more positive policies would almost certainly have emerged, both from the Department of Health, and from the BMA and Royal Colleges, if they had not been derailed by Thatcherism. It is not difficult for vigorous policies of managed competition to appear more dynamic than no policy at all, but this does not mean that other policies could not have been applied, perhaps with much better effect.

Whether hospital specialists listen to community generalists, and whether community generalists listen to their patients and the people they serve, need not depend only, or perhaps at all, on mobilising the economic pressures of consumer demand. Andrew Wall reveals the real weaknesses of the purchaser-provider split at a more general level:

"The benefits of the purchaser-provider split, now seemingly the gospel of the public services of the western world, are by no means self-evident. Organisations need to have the capacity to learn if they are to be flexible and adapt to circumstances. At a very fundamental level of work, anyone at any level of the hierarchy will have ideas about how their job could be done differently and better. The purchaser-provider split introduces something inherently unnatural because there is a forced division between those who do the job and those who plan the job ... People and organisations are motivated by the prospect of being able to have a significant say in their futures. Rob them of that, and they become lacklustre, unimaginative, and in the end obstructive, if only to attempt to recover some sense of power"[152].

He is talking about something fundamental to any serious socialist philosophy, the essence of both Karl Marx and William Morris; the difference between creative work and paid drudgery.

Can we unite those who do the job with those who plan the job?

The present purchaser-provider split applies not only to purchase through GP referral of routine specialist care at District General Hospital level, but also to purchase by DGH specialists of more highly specialised advice, interventions and support for which catchment populations of five million or more are necessary to maintain expertise and to allow reasonable economy. Given the complex and increasingly technical nature of hospital care, area commissioners would be stupid to ignore the opinions of those who actually do the work; but pushed to its logical conclusions, this is precisely what the essentially adversarial purchaser-provider split compels them to do.

A great advantage of the pre-"reform" centrally planned NHS was the balanced and rational distribution of secondary and tertiary specialist resources achieved throughout the UK by the 1970s, in marked contrast with the grossly irrational distribution of these services created by the competitive medical market in USA. As recent evidence on poorly organised cancer treatment has shown[153], the NHS still has a long way to go before general surgeons stop trying to do a bit of everything, and allow increasingly technical subspecialists to maximise health gain for patients. Such failures are not the result of rational central planning, but of peripheral resistance to it, based essentially on the lack of medical accountability guaranteed by the 1948 compromise. As all belief in such unaccountability disintegrates, the scope for rational planning must increase.

By their increasing readiness throughout the 1980s to accept the disciplines of clinical audit (objective measurements of the processes and outcomes of care of defined populations) progressive doctors, both hospital specialists and community generalists, showed their acceptance of accountability in principle. Whether their less progressive colleagues would have followed them without the coercion of the NHS "reforms" will never be known, but though progress was already rapid before "reform", the volume of audit has certainly increased much faster since. Whatever path we take in the future, this change is probably irreversible; though some may drag their feet, no doctors, specialists or generalists, are likely ever to claim a right to unaccountability in the future, or to deny that in the public interest, they must increasingly accept divisions of labour within a planned framework, providing they have opportunities to share in this planning themselves.

The foundation of accountability is truthfulness. This means that people must be allowed to measure their work themselves, or allow others to do so, without consequent reward or punishment. If the results of clinical audit are used for any purpose other than to resource deficiencies where these are found, they will become as detached from reality as the average self-administered income-tax return. The audit cycle has four component parts; agreement by the whole team on reasonable, measurable objectives; measurement of the extent to which these are actually being attained; revision of practice in the light of shortfalls revealed; and then remeasurement to assess consequent progress. This allows all workers to learn from their own measured experience, starting from any level of quality, without prior assumptions; properly resourced and with imaginative leadership, it can be enormously effective in precisely the areas of greatest need[154]. Because real (rather than legalistic) clinical accountability is a new category of thought, both professionals and the populations they serve must develop new customs to make full use of it. Local responsibility for assessment of area health needs, planning, and commissioning, shared by FHSAs, family doctors, local special interest groups such as the British Diabetic Association and Mencap, and elected representatives of the local community, could be a practical means of doing this.

12 Participative democracy

Implicitly, contracts between different units of the NHS always existed since 1948, essentially depending on hierarchies and old-boy networks, with generally passive and uncritical assent from the communities they served. The end of medical unaccountability implies the end of hierarchy and old-boy networking. What can take their place? Contracts between competing units in a market is the entrepreneurial and consumerist option. This is already resulting in promotion of the most readily industrialised and therefore most profitable clinical functions, and demotion of less profitable units serving small but important subgroups, or performing essential functions that are least easily industrialised and most dependent on communication and traditional support, such as psychiatry, geriatric and paediatric medicine. The needs of the market as perceived by managers without clinical experience do not coincide with the needs of populations, either as felt by themselves, or as seen by health professionals in daily contact with clinical realities. It is the continued dual role of family doctors as both purchasers *and* providers that makes them potentially such effective participants in area commissioning. They know what they are buying, because as junior hospital staff they had personal experience of producing it.

Sir Keith Joseph, the original theorist of Thatcherism, gave us fair warning in 1974. Speaking as Minister of Health, he proclaimed that the NHS would henceforth be run with maximum delegation of responsibility downward, and maximum accountability upward. As a patrician, his natural assumption was that doctors acquire their powers from the state, and are accountable to it for the ways they choose to use them. As a health worker, the truth always seemed to me to be the exact opposite; our power as doctors has been delegated to us by society, most readily represented by the people we serve, and our first obligation must be to them, whatever secondary obligations we may have to managers, the necessity for whom is undeniable[155]. Sir Keith's principles have now been fully applied in managed competition, with predictable results for staff morale at all levels. "It was hoped", says Professor Malcolm Forsythe, "that the contracting process would be non-legalistic, non-adversarial, and based on trust and mutual understanding. Instead, it is turning out to be bureaucratic, shrouded in mystery, and potentially damaging"[156].

The alternative is to use the inevitable and long-overdue death of medical independence to develop accountability *downwards* at all levels, both individually and collectively. For the care of individual patients, providers of tertiary (superspecialist) care should report back to providers of secondary (District General hospital) care, local specialists should report back to community generalists, and community generalists should report back to their patients as in many important ways their most informed critics. The alternative to medical independence is acceptance by all health professionals of accountability both to a necessary framework of area management for co-ordination and planning (without which no public service can operate) and to the local population, both through individual patients and through elected representatives of the local community.

In both cases, this accountability must reflect the complexity of the work with which it deals. If health professionals cannot work effectively without some kind of managerial framework, managers themselves must be accountable in some ways to health professionals; it cannot be a hierarchical relationship of the Keith Joseph kind. And if health professionals cannot produce positive health outcomes without the active participation of patients and communities in their own care, patients and communities must also accept accountability in some ways to health professionals. For care of communities as a whole, all these levels of NHS staff should be accountable to local representatives of the people, and all should have some share in needs assessment, planning, and commissioning.

Area commissioning and local government

Strategies for health are a responsibility of government. Electors must choose whether they prefer governments assisted to power by the minorities which profitably sell tobacco, diesel engines, or superfluous medicines, or by the majority which unhealthily consumes them. Implementation of these strategies must depend on people with local knowledge and loyalties, in units that bring people who plan the job together with those who do the job; not forgetting that, as we have seen, the job is done by patients as well as by health professionals. We want planned production with workers' control, the workers including all who contribute to health gain.

Community representatives should be elected by local people, not selected by Ministers from their political networks, so that if they cease to represent the people, they can be got rid of. Where can these elected representatives of the people come from? Unlike Canada and the USA, we have no tradition of local directly elected school boards. We could have directly elected members of Health Boards, sharing in area commissioning of health services at all levels, but this would require invention of an entirely new category of elected local government. The parallel with school governing is apt. Except for parent-governors, local school governing boards are at present appointed, not elected. If there were good evidence of majority participation in elections for parent governors (now exceptional, at least in working class areas) encouraging serious plans for directly elected school boards, there would be a good case for directly elected health boards also. Both the NHS and schools are subjects of intense local interest, and a good turnout of voters should be possible for both. However, unless this change occurs, elected local control would have to come from councillors selected (by their fellow councillors) for their specific interest in the NHS, but originally elected for the general responsibilities of local government.

Local government responsibility has been opposed on two main grounds. The first is the weakness of local authorities, which have been in perceived decline ever since their heyday at the close of the 19th Century. Since then central government has been enormously strengthened by changes in communication, and the experience of national mobilisation in two world wars. Fifteen years of Conservative government, steadily stripping out public responsibility for public service and replacing it by opportunities for profitable enterprise, have left councils which started with responsibility for schools, housing, and a wide range of other important local services, either without these functions entirely, or with just enough responsibility to make them credible scapegoats for inevitable failure. The real powers of local government have gone either to private entrepreneurs, or to the 73,000 or so centrally appointed nominees of quasi-non-governmental organisations (QUANGOs), more than twice the number of all elected councillors[157].

The second justification is the claim that any increase in responsibilities for local government must mean a reduction in responsibility for national government, and that the health service would therefore cease to have a uniform national character. This view has been strongly advocated by Philip Hunt, Director of the National Association of Health Authorities and Trusts (NAHAT). Experience of previous nationally planned but locally applied strategies, for example the 1944 Education Act and the post-war Housing Acts, show that this need not be so. A clear and vigorous central strategy, understood by the mass of the people, not only can but must be applied tactically by local authorities, adapting central plans to local knowledge.

The only shred of support for the contrary view comes from Nye Bevan's unexpected decision to nationalise all the hospitals in 1948, leaving them with only token elected local control, all of it now gone. As we have seen, this decision was overwhelmingly influenced by a perceived need to secure agreement from the consultants, without whom the NHS could not have gone forward at all. Though Bevan thought this a price worth paying, he never believed this undemocratic arrangement could be permanent[158], and it is totally irrelevant now.

The local government share in future area commissioning is now an important subject of public discussion, supported by David Knowles, past President of the Institute of Health Services Management, the Labour-controlled Association of Metropolitan Authorities, and by the Socialist Health Association and many others[159].

Primary Care Teams and the future of GP independent contractor status

Ever since Lloyd George nationalised club practice, GPs have been independent contractors — private purveyors of public service. The consequence was cheap but all too often nasty primary care. Because patient care was financed through the same pocket as GP's mortgages, cars, holidays, and the education of their children, whatever was spent was usually the least which a poorly informed and undemanding population made possible.

As governments were forced (by escalating hospital costs) to recognise the value of good primary care, they began to recognise the risks of a system so cheap that it was positively dangerous; but every attempt to increase investment in primary care ran up against the same difficulty. The health needs and professional difficulties of general practice were always greatest where professional incomes (from all sources) were lowest, and the apparently best, and best paid, practices were mostly in areas of least health need, most attractive to professionals.

The most effective national investment in primary care ever made was the 1966 Doctors' Charter, devised by the Medical Practitioners' Union (mainly by a notable and recently deceased SHA member, Dr Hugh Faulkner), and implemented by the late Sir James Cameron for the BMA and Health Minister Kenneth Robinson for the Wilson Labour government. It partially overcame the difficulty by earmarking new funds so that they had to be spent on patient care, and were not a part of GPs' income. However, to limit demand, these were still for the most part linked to some investment by GPs themselves, in what were still regarded as their own businesses. They still had to meet 30% of employed staff salaries, and to make large personal investments in subsidised new buildings, rewarded by huge eventual profits in areas of high employment and rising property values, but an impossible risk in areas of economic decline. This was originally mitigated by a wave of health centre building in the 1970s, but this ceased with the beginning of Conservative rule in 1979.

By 1989, most progressive practices were already working in purpose built premises (NHS-owned health centres or GP-built) and employed their full reimbursable complement of staff. They had used all the resources available for new initiatives. But because of independent contractor status, these subsidised investments went preferentially to areas where prospects were good — areas with least unemployment and rising property values[160, 161, 162, 163], and lowest morbidity and social need.

Because of independent contractor status, before NHS "reform", progressive practice where it was most needed depended on innovation by a minority of exceptional doctors, committed in principle to a socialised service even if they had to finance much of this themselves. The "reforms" have enabled enlightened FHSAs to commission specified work from GPs and thus provide resources for innovation of this kind, including work previously undertaken in hospital out-patient departments. But this was more an effect of larger budgets, better qualified administrators, and a general destabilisation allowing greater discretionary powers, than a direct effect of the purchaser-provider split itself. Though independent contractor status made it easy for progressive GPs to give priority to social responsibility rather than the needs of their own families, it made it equally easy for most to do the opposite.

The SHA has always believed in salaried status for all doctors in public service. All hospital doctors are salaried, and until the market "reforms" there was never any example of interference by management in clinical decisions. More importantly, all members of primary care teams other than GP principals are salaried, for whom the self-employed entrepreneurial status of GPs is an anomaly often open to more cynical interpretations than most GPs realise. Independent contractor status is a hangover from the past, when GPs in industrial areas were seldom more, and often somewhat less, than shopkeepers. Opposition to salaried service has come from doctors who fear (now with some justification) loss of clinical autonomy to managers who do not share their objectives or understand the nature of their work, and from the Treasury which fears (also with some justification) a rapid rise in the cost of primary care, as GPs cease to have a personal stake in underfunding the service.

Sooner or later, any government that is serious about developing a more rational and therefore more cost-effective NHS, will have to face up to the need for a salaried service for NHS general practice. To minimise opposition and for natural justice, this must be generous enough to maintain incomes at least as they now are. This will entail a large additional investment in primary care, but as a much larger investment in primary care is already necessary on other grounds, which cannot be targeted on the areas most in need without separation of earnings from investment, this must be seen as a necessary consequence of any serious step toward a more rational, and therefore more cost-effective, NHS.

We have good evidence that though only about 7% of GPs say they would prefer a salaried service to independent contractor status, another 44% would consider the possibility seriously; less than half (48%) are now definitely hostile to salaried status, and among GP trainees, 73% would either prefer or consider the possibility of salaried status[164]. There is more support for salary now than at any time since 1948. Introduction of such a service could be at least initially selective, in areas of highest health need, with the worst problems of GP recruitment, where support for salaries is greatest and where most experience of locality commissioning has already been gained. There is already long experience of generally successful salaried general practice in Quebec Province and Oslo, and more recent experience in Finland, all in countries with medical and social cultures similar to our own. Plans at least for widespread experiment on these lines are certainly feasible[165], and should be a part of Labour's next election programme.

Primary care teams of the future

Rational reform of the NHS depends above all on reform of its foundation in primary care. Scattered all over the UK, there are now primary care teams already attempting to deliver the full fruits of medical science to all who can benefit, not as a business but as a free public service. They remain exceptional, but there is no Region without them. These are areas already liberated from commerce, so far as that is possible in a consumerist society. Their experience is the best guide we can have, as we grope forward to a better and more sharing society of the near future — feasible socialism.

From 1961 to 1987, I was in charge of a mining village practice in South Wales uniquely fitted to serve as a descriptive, and to some extent an experimental model of the basic production units on which the NHS is built. Relationships with other practices and home care units in the Afan valley, and routine referral patterns to local hospitals, were simple and easily accessible to analysis. We had the first health centre in Wales in 1966, and began systematic audit of an increasing range of clinical and economic indicators from 1968 onwards. By the early 1980s, we had a very substantial body of data, which though limited to a population of only about 2,000, covered an exceptionally long period, and included records of people who had moved away or died. From 1983 onward, we tried to interest various health economists and independent health policy foundations in this data set, as a model from which we might learn useful lessons about the audited, rational, continuing anticipatory community care of the future[166]. We failed; most health economists believe they have emancipated their subject from political economy, to achieve a value-free methodology valid throughout space and time, so they are not attracted by real human material which makes such beliefs difficult. However, even without skilled economic assistance, we learned a great deal.

First, we learned that in the early 1980s, although the NHS economy was in a remarkably healthy state by any international standard, nobody knew the price of anything we used, except prescribed medication. Neither our regional hospital laboratory, nor the X-ray department, could supply any even approximately priced menus from which to cost our demands on them. They knew their global costs, but were unable to break them down into any of the units relevant to our clinical decisions. All they could suggest was that we look at the tariffs used by the British United Provident Association or by hospitals in USA, to charge their private patients, but these included a large profit component, absent at that time from the NHS.

Knowing that money always represents somebody's labour, and knowing the value of our own, we were concerned to provide an economic service. Wasteful medicine is not just expensive, but dangerous, and bad science. To discover what was actually going on in our practice, we had to apply more and more measurements — blood pressures, weights for height, smoking consumption and blood carbon monoxide levels, tablet counts to measure compliance, glycated haemoglobin to assess diabetes, peak flow rates to assess asthma, patients' diaries to assess epilepsy — you name it, we measured it. The more we measured real health values, the less we needed to concern ourselves with price, because the result was the same; extravagant care is not only expensive but dangerous, thoughtful care is not only safer, but cheaper in all respects but one — it needs more time.

Second, we learned that planned, audited, continuing anticipatory care of whole communities almost certainly does produce much greater health gain than unplanned care which simply reacts to presented demand, within customary expectations. Comparing death rates under 65 for our health centre with those for another serving a similar population in the same valley over the same period 1981-6[167], ours were 68% lower than for the control health centre. All the main health risks we targeted (cigarette smoking, blood pressure, weight-for-height, and glycated haemoglobin in diabetics) showed substantial falls. These health gains were achieved in a community ranked fourth from the bottom on the Townsend index of social deprivation, out of 55 local authorities in West Glamorgan, which since 1970 has probably had the worst male unemployment figures in Britain.

Finally, we learned that this all takes time, and sustained personal commitment. For community generalists at least, virtually nothing can be achieved in less than five years; but equally, there is almost no reasonable target that cannot be reached in a working lifetime of 30 years.

Similar lessons could be drawn from the experience of many other progressive primary care teams following similar paths. The morale, goodwill, and sense of vocation of health workers of all grades was the most valuable of all NHS assets, and its near-destruction is the greatest crime of the market "reformers".

13 Feasible Socialism

The fundamental difference between the Labour and Conservative Parties lies in their opposite aims for future society, how our children and grandchildren will live. Socialists cannot believe that any society worth living in will be possible, without fundamental change toward an economy of co-operation and sharing, rather than an endless fight of every man against every man, with all condemned to be either heartless winners or miserable losers, with most talents and imaginations wasted.

In 1945, we thought we knew. From 1940 to 1945, centralised command economies in Britain, USA, and the USSR proved able to perform all sorts of miracles, which we had all been told were impossible before the war. We would use essentially the same means, the same defiance of economic laws devised by bankers in their own interest; the same determination to subordinate money, a human invention, to human ends; the same confidence that property is less important than life, and that nobody has a right to dispose of the jobs and futures of thousands of others, merely because this suits the ends of directors or shareholders. That high tide of economic democracy, demanded as a necessary sequel to political democracy, formed the NHS as its apparently unimportant by-product, far less significant to every contemporary observer than nationalisation of the coal industry, or other "commanding heights" of the economy.

Now even the memory of those high expectations has almost vanished. The NHS is virtually all we have left. Refounded on a new base of participative democracy, how could the NHS contribute to such wider social change?

To all who actually believe in society, even to "One Nation" Tories who realise that the war of every man against every man can only be sustained within some framework of shared human values, the NHS as a free and equal public service, not as a competitive business, is essential for social survival. Just as nineteenth century society had to declare a truce on Sundays, when people who had thieved and swindled so far as the law allowed on weekdays, could re-establish some self-respect among their fellows, the NHS now provides an area in which we can still relate to each other as members of a single species, with equal rights to such life and health as blind providence allows us. Unlimited pursuit of profit leads to an intolerably divided society, hateful to socialists because they know it is unnecessary, but also dangerous and disturbing to conservatives with enough intelligence and sensitivity to understand that winners in their society differ from losers much less than they like to imagine.

We therefore have a huge base of popular support for any policy that moves the NHS back on course, away from competitive business and back to universal public service. And the evidence deployed in this book guarantees that, for once, the interests of social justice and of economic viability are the same. Medical science will continue to grow, but sustainable growth in the NHS sufficient to apply this science to all who need it will certainly not be possible if health workers continue to be subordinated to managerial visions of efficient production of medical care as an industrial commodity, passively consumed by an increasingly demanding public. A re-socialised service will not necessarily be cheaper than what we now have, because years of systematic under-investment must be corrected, but costs can certainly rise far more slowly in a co-operative than a competitive service, in which both staffs and patients are once again encouraged to help each other, and to understand the great complexity of even the simplest problems in human biology.

The fuller use of human intelligence, wider clinical autonomy and professionalisation for health workers of all grades, and far greater use of the intelligence and imagination of patients, carers, and parents in continuing management of chronic disorders, could bring huge economies to the service. This unused energy cannot be released quickly. It depends mainly on micro-economic changes at the level of personal consultation both in primary care and in hospitals. However, medical and nursing professionals are now generally ready for such changes, which could have large macro-economic effects within five years, mainly through more thoughtful prescribing and less translation of psycho-social problems into costly but futile somatisation.

Above all, we must re-assert the human right to effective care in its widest sense, for all according to need. Everyone thought this was a permanent gain in 1948. This right has been steadily eroded since the Conservatives took office in 1979. In 1984, 30% of long-term nursing care was provided by the NHS; by 1994, this had fallen to 10%. The rest was, and is, provided by means-tested nursing homes, run either by local authorities as a public service, or by private entrepreneurs, who are now guaranteed at least 85% of the means-tested market. Without any public discussion or mandate, Conservative governments have steadily and stealthily shifted the NHS from its traditions of curing where possible, but caring always, to become so far as possible a repair service, without responsibility for continuing care. Which of the many exciting new innovations aimed at cure will actually work, time alone will tell; but we already know the effectiveness of long-term nursing care and support, relief of pain, and housing, dressing, feeding, washing, cleaning, and generally encouraging sick people, often near the end of their lives. These are services all of us want for ourselves if and when our time comes. Make no mistake, we want genuine advances in medical science to be applied as widely as possible, but this can only be done on a secure foundation of continuing care.

We fully realise the huge cost implications of such a commitment, the difficulties this will represent when a Labour government is elected to undo the damage inflicted on our economy and culture by almost two decades of every man for himself, and the consequent constraints on opposition policy. That is why the Labour movement still needs the SHA today, as an independent socialist conscience to remind all of us of the real purpose of all our efforts.

The NHS as model for a future economy

For Socialists, a democratised NHS has far greater potential

significance. Many Conservatives honestly believed that remodelling this huge public service in the image of competitive manufacturing industry was bound to give taxpayers better value for money. Though the NHS was indeed the envy of the post-war world, the same could hardly be said for British manufacturing industry. Predictably, the experiment has failed. Nobody likes it, except people well paid to do so. People are different from motor cars.

But not so different that the car industry has nothing to learn from the NHS. The NHS has a socially useful product, both personal and social: health gain for all. This can, with some difficulty and imagination, be measured. It *must* be measured, for us to avoid the fatal error of using easily counted clinical interventions as a convenient, but from all historical experience grossly misleading, proxy for health gain. Why should this not eventually be true also of the transport industry, that is, the entire ragbag of motor manufacturers, bicycle makers, their retailers, road and rail construction and maintenance, railway engine and rolling stock manufacture and maintenance, airports and aircraft, travel agents, road hauliers, town planners, removal vans, ferries, in fact every part of the economy mainly concerned with mobility? The socially useful product of this presently un-coordinated and unplanned concatenation of competing industries could be gains in mobility for all, personal and social. But this is not how the transport industry is either seen or organised. The common aim of all its un-coordinated parts is to maximise profit, often by driving some other part of the industry out of business, through sale of competing products. In the case of car sales, we have the nonsensical situation that in the absence of any overall transport policy, and with continued decline of all forms of public transport, each new car produced and sold actually *reduces* the overall mobility of the population, and every industrial success brings our cities closer to gridlock.

Manufacturing industry as presently conceived, in advancing Germany, Japan, and South-east Asia no less than decaying Britain, presents no useful model for reform of the NHS. But as a centrally co-ordinated nationalised industry serving social need rather than private greed, open to peripheral innovation at its community base with a growing element of participative democracy, the NHS will one day present a useful model for eventually socialised manufacturing industry.

For serious politics, for the future of our children and grandchildren, the timetable of social change is relatively unimportant. What is supremely important is not the speed but the direction of change; forward to sharing, or backward to grabbing. In this battle the NHS has been driven to the very centre of serious politics, and there it will remain, a core of custom and practice around which a more dignified society will one day be built — starting not with the commanding heights of our economy, but the commanding depths of our culture.

Appendices

Appendix1

Figure 1. Total expenditure on medical and nursing care as percent of Gross National Product in 22 OECD countries, 1975 and 1987, ranked by total cost % GNP 1987.

	1975	1987
USA	8.4	11.2
Sweden	8.0	9.0
Canada	7.3	8.6
France	6.8	8.6
Netherlands	7.7	8.5
Austria	7.3	8.4
Germany	7.8	8.2
Iceland	5.9	7.8
Switz'	7.0	7.7
Norway	6.7	7.5
Irish Republic	7.7	7.4
Finland	6.3	7.4
Belgium	5.8	7.2
Australia	5.7	7.1

	1975	1987
USA	8.4	11.2
New Zealand	6.4	6.9
Italy	5.8	6.9
Japan	5.5	6.8
Portugal	6.4	6.4
UK	5.5	6.1
Denmark	6.5	6.0
Spain	5.1	6.0
Greece	4.1	5.3

Appendix 2

Figure 2. Public expenditure as % total expenditure, 22 OECD countries, 1975 and 1987, ranked by public expenditure as % GNP 1987.

	1975	1987		1975	1987
Norway	95	99	Norway	95	99
Sweden	90	91	Greece	61	75
Iceland	90	88	**Japan**	73	73
UK	91	87	Australia	63	72
Denmark	92	87	Spain	71	72
Irish Republic	83	86	Austria	76	68
New Zealand	84	83	Switz'	68	67
France	76	78	Portugal	59	61
Finland	79	78	**USA**	43	41
Italy	86	78			
Netherlands	77	78			
Germany	79	77			
Belgium	79	76			
Canada	77	75			

Figs 1 and 2 from Table 1, Schieber GJ, Poullier J-P. Overview of international comparisons of health care expenditures. OECD Policy Studies No.7 *Health care systems in transition*. Paris: OECD 1990. pp.9-15.

References

1. Shaw GB. Preface to *The Doctor's Dilemma*. London: John Constable 1907.
2. Hart JT. *A new kind of doctor: the general practitioner's part in the health of the community*. London: Merlin Press 1988. ISBN 0 85036 299 7.
3. Murray DS. *Why a National Health Service?* London: Pemberton Books 1971. ISBN 0 301 71121 6.
4. Bevan A. *In place of fear*. London: Heinemann 1952. This is now hard to find. There is an excellent collection of his speeches and writing on the NHS in Charles Webster's *Aneurin Bevan on the National Health Service*. Oxford: Wellcome Unit for the History of Medicine 1991. ISBN 0 906844 09 6.
5. Dr Alfred Cox, former Chairman of the BMA, writing in the British Medical Journal 1946;**i**:541, "after a careful reading of the Bill". Fearful of repeating the BMA's ignominious rout in 1912 when its boycott of the Lloyd George Act failed utterly, two months before the appointed day he advised dignified retreat. Like the other BMA leaders, he never apologised for his contribution to anti-NHS hysteria.
6. Speech to the Special Representative Body of the BMA, 17.3.48, reported in the British Medical Journal.
7. Appendix Tables 15 & 16. OECD Policy Studies No.7 *Health care systems in transition.* Paris: OECD 1990. pp.143-4.
8. Himmelstein D, Woolhandler S. Cost without benefit. New England Journal of Medicine 1986;314:441-5.
9. *Health 2000: the health and wealth of the nation in the 21st century.* London: Labour Party, 1994. ISBN 0 86117 221.
10. Pope C. Waiting times for outpatient appointments. British Medical Journal 1993;**306**:408-9.
11. German K, Nuwahid F, Matthews P, Stephenson T. Dangers of long waiting times for outpatient appointments at a urology clinic. British Medical Journal 1993;**306**:429.
12. Coulter A, McPherson K. Socioeconomic variations in the use of common surgical operations. British Medical Journal 1985;**291**:183-7.

13. Dickman RL, Bukowski S. Epidemiology and ethics of coronary artery bypass surgery in an Eastern county. Journal of Family Practice 1982;**14**:233-9.
14. Gould JB. Socioeconomic differences in rates of caesarean section. New England Journal of Medicine 1989;**321**:233-9.
15. Bunker JP, Brown B. The physician as an informed consumer of surgical services. New England Journal of Medicine 1974;**290**:1051-5.
16. Bombardier C, Fuchs VR, Lillard LA, Warner KE. Socioeconomic factors affecting the utilization of surgical operations. New England Journal of Medicine 1977;**297**:699-705.
17. Scott HD, Mackie A. Decisions to hospitalize and operate: a socioeconomic perspective in an urban state. Surgery 1975;**77**:311-7.
18. Bunker JP, Brown B. op. cit.
19. Marx K. *Critique of the Gotha programme: marginal notes to the programme of the German workers' Party*. Written 1875, first published Neue Zeit 1891. Karl Marx, selected works vol.2, Moscow: Foreign Languages Publishing House 1942.
20. Quoted in British Medical Journal 1991;**303**:798.
21. Brody H. The lie that heals: the ethics of giving placebos. Annals of Internal Medicine 1982;**97**:112-8.
22. Webster C. The health services since the war. Vol.1. *Problems of health care: the National health Service before 1957.* London: HMSO 1988. ISBN 0-11-630942-3.
23. Neale J. *Memoirs of a callous picket: working for the NHS.* London: Pluto Press 1983.
24. Eisenberg L. Science in medicine: too much, or too little and too limited in scope? American Journal of Medicine 1988;**84**:483-91.
25. Hampton JR, Harrison MJG, Mitchell JRA, Prichard JS, Seymour C. Relative contributions of history-taking, physical examination, and laboratory investigation to diagnosis and management of medical outpatients. British Medical Journal 1975;**ii**:486-9.
26. Horder JP, Moore G. The consultation and health outcomes. British Journal of General Practice 1990;**40**:442-3.
27. Hart JT. Rule of halves: implications of increasing diagnosis and reducing dropout for future workload and prescribing costs in primary care. British Journal of General Practice 1992;**42**:116-9.
28. Hart JT, Thomas C, Gibbons B, Edwards C, Hart M, Jones J, Jones M, Walton P. Twenty five years of audited screening in a socially deprived community. British Medical Journal 1991;**302**:1509-13.
29. Charlton BG, Calvert N, White M et al. Health promotion priorities for general practice: constructing and using "indicative prevalences". British Medical Journal 1994;**308**:1019-22.
30. Joyce CRB, Caple G, Mason M, Reynolds E, Mathews JA. Quantitative study of doctor-patient communication. Quarterly Journal of Medicine 1969;**38**:183-94.
31. Buchan IC, Richardson IM. *Time study of consultations in general practice.* Scottish Health Studies No.27. Edinburgh: Scottish Home & Health Department 1973.
32. Beckman HB, Frankel RM. The effect of physician behavior on the collection of data. Annals of Internal Medicine 1984;**101**:692-6.
33. Tuckett D, Boulton M, Olson C, Williams A. *Meetings between experts: an approach to sharing ideas in medical consultations.* London: Tavistock Publications 1985.
34. Morrell DC, Evans ME, Morris RW, Roland MO. The five-minute consultation: effect of time constraint on clinical content and patient satisfaction. British Medical Journal 1986;**292**:870-3.
35. Wilson A, McDonald P, Hayes L, Cooney J. Health promotion in the general practice consultation: a minute makes a difference. British Medical Journal 1992;**304**:227-30.
36. Savage R, Armstrong D. Effect of a general practitioner's consulting style on patients' satisfaction: a controlled study. British Medical Journal 1990;**301**:968-70.
37. Albutt C. The Act and the future of medicine. Letter to *The Times* 3 January 1912.

38. Finnerty FA, Mattie EC, Finnerty FA. Hypertension in the inner city. I. Analysis of dropouts. Circulation 1973;**47**:73-6.

39. Finnerty FA, Shaw LW, Hinnelsback CK. Hypertension in the inner city. II . Circulation 1973;**47**:76-80.

40. Hjortdahl P, Borchgrevink CF. Continuity of care: influence of general practitioners' knowledge about their patients on use of resources in consultations. British Medical Journal 1991;**303**:1181-4.

41. Charlton BG. Stories of sickness. British Journal of General Practice 1991;**41**:222-3.

42. Electoral Reform Ballot Services. Survey Report to the General Medical Services Committee of the BMA 1992. Tables 22, 23.

43. Moss F, McNicol M. London after Tomlinson: secondary care beyond Tomlinson: an opportunity to be seized or squandered? British Medical Journal 1992;**305**:1211-4.

44. Personal communication from Professor David Metcalfe. The 1962 and 1976 referral figures are for GP referrals only, 1986 figures include cross-referrals from other hospital departments. The falling trend is therefore, if anything, understated.

45. Hayes TM, Harries J. Randomized controlled trial of routine hospital clinic care versus routine general practice care for type II diabetes. British Medical Journal 1984;**289**:728-30.

46. Day JL, Humphreys H, Alban-Davies H. Problems of comprehensive shared diabetes care. British Medical Journal 1987;**294**:1590-2.

47. Wilkes E, Lawton E. The diabetic, the hospital, and primary care. Journal of the Royal College of General Practitioners 1980;**30**:199-206.

48. Diabetes Integrated Care Evaluation Team. Integrated care for diabetes: clinical, psychosocial, and economic evaluation. British Medical Journal 1994;**308**:1208-12.

49. Riddle MC. A strategy for chronic disease. Lancet 1980;ii:734-6.

50. Hollis JF, Lichtenstein E, Mount K et al. Nurse-assisted smoking counselling in medical settings: minimising demands on physicians. Preventive Medicine 1991;**20**:497-507.

51. Vogt TM, Lichtenstein E, Hollis J et al. Integrating effective tobacco interventions into the routine delivery of medical care. Presented to the 8th World Conference on Tobacco or Health; April 1, 1992; Buenos Aires.

52. Fries JF, Crapo LM. *Vitality and aging.* San Francisco: WH Freeman 1981. ISBN 0-7167-1308-X.

53. Hart JT. Two paths for medical practice. Lancet 1992;**340**:772-5.

54. Wilkinson RG (ed.) *Class and health: research and longitudinal data.* London: Tavistock 1986.

55. Relman AS. The new medical-industrial complex. New England Journal of Medicine 1980;**303**:963-70.

56. Relman AS. Practising medicine in the new business climate. New England Journal of Medicine 1987;**317**:1150-7.

57. Relman AS. Assessment and accountability: the third revolution in medical care. New England Journal of Medicine 1988;**319**:1220-2.

58. Lancet editorial. US health reforms: clichés, cost, and Mrs.C. Lancet 1993;**341**:791-2.

59. Enthoven A. *Reflections on the management of the National Health Service: an American looks at incentives to efficiency in health services management in the UK.* Occasional Papers no.5. London: Nuffield Provincial Hospitals Trust, 1985.

60. Glaser WA. The competition vogue and its outcomes. Lancet 1993;**341**:805-12.

61. Harrigan P. Australia: privatisation of NSW public hospital system. Lancet 1992;**339**:921.

62. Ragg M. Proposals for Australian health insurance reforms. Lancet 1994;**343**:47-8.

63. Saltman RB, von Otter C. *Planned markets and public competition.* Buckingham: Open University Press 1992.

64. Dorozynski A. France finally agrees on health shake-up. British Medical Journal 1993;**307**:889.

65. Genillard A. Germany's health care system soars back into the black. British Medical Journal 1993;**307**:700.

66. Siegel J. Israel at medical crossroads. British Medical Journal 1992;**305**:441.
67. Keates T. Italy's health services: now for the real reforms? Lancet 1993;**342**:733.
68. Sheldon T. Health care access under threat in Netherlands. British Medical Journal 1993;**307**:1230-1.
69. Buchan H. New Zealand's health care reforms. British Medical Journal 1993;**307**:635-6.
70. Coney S. Asset-stripping New Zealand's elderly people. Lancet 1994;**343**:591.
71. Baños JE. Spain: the Abril Report. Lancet 1992;**339**:799-800.
72. Navarro V. Spain's health care. Lancet 1992;**339**:1234.
73. Nilsson M. Sweden's health reform. Lancet 1993;**342**:979.
74. Deacon B (ed.) *The new Eastern Europe: social policy past, present and future.* London: Sage Publications 1992 ISBN 0-8039-8439-1.
75. Ruderman AP. Economic adjustment and the future of health services in the Third World. Journal of Public Health Policy 1990;**11**:*481-90.*
76. LaFond AK. When the money runs out. Lancet 1994;**343**:371-2.
77. Diderichsen F. Why Sweden copied the NHS reforms. In Iliffe S (ed). Health Care and the Common Market. Proceedings of the 8th IAHP (Europe) Conference 1993. London: IAHP/Medical World 1994. pp.16-18.
78. Waitzkin H. The strange career of managed competition: military failure to medical success? Journal of the American Public Health Association 1994;**84**:482-9.
79. Enthoven AC. Choosing strategies and selecting weapons systems (address before the Naval War College, Newport, RI, June 6 1963). In Tucker SA (ed.) *A modern design for defense decision: a MacNamara-Hitch-Enthoven anthology.* Washington DC: Industrial College of the Armed Forces, 1966.
80. Doll WRS. Monitoring the National Health Service. Journal of the Royal Society of Medicine 1973;**66**:729-40.
81. Enthoven A. *International comparisons of health care systems: what can Europeans learn from Americans?* pp.57-71 in OECD Social Policy Studies No.7 Health care systems in transition. Paris: OECD 1990.
82. Friedman M, Friedman RD. *Capitalism and freedom.* Chicago: University of Chicago Press, 1962.
83. British Medical Journal 1990;**300**:1081.
84. Brecht B. *The life of Galileo.* London: Methuen 1968.
85. Lock S. Realities — and (some) visions: not all gloom at Godber symposium. British Medical Journal 1993;**307**:280.
86. Beecham L. Mutiny on the flagship. British Medical Journal 1990;**300**:417-8.
87. Delamothe T. Consultants say no to self governing trusts. British Medical Journal 1990;**300**:1539.
88. *Health Service Journal* 19.9.91.
89. Warden J. The manager is king. British Medical Journal 1991;**302**:1298.
90. Jones RR. Health as a political issue. *Guardian* 24.2.93
91. Smith J. Guy's will stop acute care. British Medical Journal 1994;**308**:496.
92. Dyer O. Charities demand money back in Guy's changeover. British Medical Journal 1994;**308**:496.
93. Dean M. Do we need fewer doctors and nurses? Lancet 1993;**341**:1401.
94. Warden J. Beginning of the end state NHS. British Medical Journal 1990;**301**:199.
95. Caines E. Time to put our NHS in the trust. *Guardian* 3.9.93.
96. Caines E. Amputation is crucial to the patient's health. Political cowardice is denying the NHS the medicine it needs: fewer professionals and greater productivity. *Guardian* 11.5.93
97. Blunkett D. Equity, prevention and accountability — a socialist agenda for the 21st century. In: Iliffe S, Mostyn J, Ross R (eds). From market chaos to common sense: papers on future policies for health. Medical World/Socialist Health Association 1993.
98. Culyer AJ, Maynard AK, Posnett JW. *Competition in health care: reforming the NHS.* Houndsmills, Hants: Macmillan, 1990.

99. Galbraith JK. *A history of economics: the past as the present.* London: Hamish Hamilton, 1987.

100. Acheson ED. The impending crisis of old age: a challenge to ingenuity. Lancet 1982;**ii**:592-4.

101. Dean M. Who looks after granny? Lancet 1992;**339**:294-5.

102. Henwood M. *Through a glass darkly: community care and elderly people.* London: King's Fund Institute 1992.

103. Brindle D. Bed bugbears: where does free National Health Service Care end and paid-for care begin? *Guardian* 16.3.94

104. Brindle D. Care ruling "could cost NHS dear". *Guardian* 3.2.94.

105. Dean M. Moral panic in a moral maze. Lancet 1993;**341**:746-7.

106. Isaacs B. Geriatric patients: do their families care? British Medical Journal 1971;**4**:282-6.

107. Jones DA, Vetter NJ. Formal and informal support received by carers of elderly dependents. British Medical Journal 1985;**291**:643-5.

108. Christie B. Dementia in Scotland. British Medical Journal 1991;**302**:1563. Review of Dementia in Scotland: agenda for action. Edinburgh: Scottish Action on Dementia 1991.

109. Brindle D. Community care "failing to improve lot of carers". *Guardian* 3.5.94. Review of *Community Care: just a fairy tale?* Carers' National Association, 20-25 Glasshouse Yard, London EC1A 4JS 1994.

110. Challis L, Henwood M. Equity in community care. British Medical Journal 1994;**308**:1496-8.

111. OECD Policy Studies No.7 Health care systems in transition. Paris: OECD 1990. Table 43, p.177.

112. Russell RCG. Minimally invasive surgery: biliary surgery. British Medical Journal 1993;**307**:1266-9.

113. Banta HD. Minimally invasive surgery: implications for hospitals, health workers and patients. British Medical Journal 1993;**397**:1546-9.

114. Gagner M, Begin E, Hurteau R et al. Robotic interactive laparoscopic cholecystectomy. Lancet 1994;**343**:596-7.

115. ECRI. Out-patient surgery: its perils and prospects. Health Technology 1987;**1**:91-8.

116. Whickham JEA. Minimally invasive surgery: future developments. British Medical Journal 1994;**308**:193-6.

117. Labour Research Department. NHS beds cut. LRD Fact Service 1994:**56**:12.

118. Schieber GJ, Poullier J-P. Overview of international comparisons of health care expenditures. OECD Policy Studies No.7 *Health care systems in transition.* Paris: OECD 1990. pp.9-15.

119. Ibid, Table 4.

120. Annals of Surgery 1993;**218**:129-37.

121. American Journal of Surgery 1993;**165**:387-548.

122. Orlando R, Russell JC, Lynch J et al. Laparoscopic cholecystectomy: a statewide experience. Archives of Surgery 1993;**128**:494-9.

123. McPherson K, Strong PM, Jones L et al. Do cholecystectomy rates correlate with geographical variations in the prevalence of gallstones? Journal of Epidemiology & Community Health 1985;**39**:179-182.

124. Johnson AG. Gallstones: the real issues. British Medical Journal 1993;**306**:1114-5.

125. Godfrey PJ, Bates T, Harrison M et al. Gallstones and mortality: a study of all gallstone related deaths in a single health district. Gut 1984;**25**:1029-33.

126. Gracie WA, Ranschoff DF. The natural history of silent gallstones: the innocent gallstone is not a myth. N Engl J Med 1982;**307**:794-800.

127. Ranshoff DF, Gracie WA, Wolfensen LB et al. Prophylactic cholecystectomy or expectant management for silent gallstones. Annals of Internal Medicine 1983;**99**:199-204.

128. Bainton D, Davies G, Evans K, Gravelle I. Gallbladder disease prevalence in a South Wales industrial town. New England Journal of Medicine 1976;**294**:1147-9.
129. Wennberg JE, McPherson K, Caper P. Will payment based on diagnosis-related groups control hospital costs? New England Journal of Medicine 1984;**311**:295-300.
130. Barker DJP, Gardner MJ, Power C et al. Prevalence of gallstones at necropsy in nine British towns. British Medical Journal 1979;**ii**:1389-92.
131. Evans RG, Barer ML. The American predicament. OECD Policy Studies No.7 *Health care systems in transition.* Paris: OECD 1990. pp.80-5.
132. National Association of Health Authorities & Trusts. *Reinventing health care — towards a new model.* Birmingham: NAHAT 1993.
133. Hart. The problem of beds. British Medical Journal 1993;**307**:1026.
134. Thorn PA, Russell RG. Diabetic clinics today and tomorrow: mini-clinics in general practice. British Medical Journal 1973;**ii**:534-6.
135. Diabetes Integrated Care Evaluation Team 1994, op. cit.
136. Petrie JC, Robb OJ, Webster J et al. Computer assisted shared care in hypertension. British Medical Journal 1985;**290**:1960-3.
137. Hart JT, Thomas C, Gibbons B, Edwards C, Hart M, Jones J, Jones M, Walton P 1991 Op.cit.
138. Hart JT. Opportunities and risks of local population research in general practice. In: Gray DJP (ed.) *Forty years on: the story of the first forty years of the Royal College of General Practitioners.* London: RCGP 1992. pp.199-204.
139. Glasman D. Eyes right for the new FPC line up. Health Service Journal 1990;**100**:10-11.
140. *Health 2000.* Op. cit.
141. Electoral Reform Ballot Services 1992, op. cit.
142. Hart JT. The Inverse Care Law. Lancet 1971;**i**:405-12.
143. *GP fundholding: bad for your health.* London: Labour Party, 1993.
145. Medicopolitical digest: GP fundholders control £1.8bn of spending power. British Medical Journal 1994;**308**:1242.
146. Gibbons BJ. Primary care-led commissioning. Medical World 1992;**(7)**:25-6.
147. Medical Practitioners' Union. Before you consider fundholding, consider the alternatives. MPU 1993.
148. Honigsbaum F. *The division in British medicine: a history of the separation of general practice from hospital care 1911-1968.* New York: St.Martin's Press, 1979. ISBN 0 312 21431 6.
149. Hart JT. *A new kind of doctor: the general practitioner's part in the health of the community.* London: Merlin Press 1988. ISBN 0 85036 299 7.
151. Allsop J, May A. *The emperor's new clothes: Family Practitioner Committees in the 1980s.* London: King's Fund 1986.
152. Wall A. Reforming the reforms In: Iliffe S, Mostyn J, Ross R (eds). *From market chaos to common sense: papers on future policies for health.* Medical World/Socialist Health Association 1993.
153. Dillner L. Cancer services to be radically redeveloped in Britain. British Medical Journal 1994;**308**:1317.
154. Johnson R. Where have all the pennies gone? The work of the Manchester Medical Audit Advisory Group. British Medical Journal 1994;**309**:98-102.
155. Hart JT. Delegation upwards, accountability downwards. Medical Week 29.3.74.
156. Forsythe M. Commissioning specialist services. British Medical Journal 1993;**306**:872-3.
157. Extragovernmental organisations in the UK and their accountability. Charter 88 Trust, Exmouth House, 311 Pine Street, London EC1R 0JH.
158. Bevan A. The future of the hospital services, 5 October 1945 (p.37) and Local government management of the hospitals, 12 March 1954 (pp.195-201). In, Webster C. *Aneurin Bevan on the National Health Service.* Oxford: Wellcome Unit for the History of Medicine 1991. ISBN 0 906844 09 6.

159. Socialist Health Association model resolution for submission to the 1994 Labour Party Conference. *Future governance of the NHS.* London: SHA 24.5.94.

160. Bosanquet N, Leese B. Family doctors and innovation in general practice. British Medical Journal 1988;**296**:1576-80.

161. Bosanquet N, Leese B. Family doctors: their choice of practice strategy. British Medical Journal 1986;**293**:667-70.

162. Bosanquet N. Quality of care in general practice — lessons from the past. Journal of the Royal College of General Practitioners 1989;**39**:88-90.

163. Bosanquet N, Leese B. *Family doctors and economic incentives.* Aldershot: Gower Publishing, 1989.

164. Electoral Reform Ballot Services. Survey Report to the General Medical Services Committee of the BMA 1992.

165. Iliffe S. Thinking through a salaried service for general practice. British Medical Journal 1992;**304**:1546-7.

166. Hart JT. Hidden agendas of earlier diagnosis. In Zander L (ed.) *Change: the challenge for the future.* RCGP Annual Symposium 1983. London: RCGP 1984. pp.54-63.

167. Hart JT, Thomas C, Gibbons B, Edwards C, Hart M, Jones J, Jones M, Walton P 1991 Op.cit.

Glossary

Acute Of sudden onset and short duration

Anticipatory care Continuing medical care in which health professionals not only attend to patients' wants but are also on the lookout for present and future needs

Caesarean section Delivery of a baby by cutting open the uterus.

Cholecystectomy Removal of the gallbladder

Chronic Of slow onset and long duration

Day-cases Patients admitted to hospital for treatment who return home the same day

Elective Planned in advance

Emergency admissions Admissions to hospital that are not planned in advance

Endoscopy Use of an endoscope, a flexible telescope that can be introduced either through a natural opening (such as the mouth or rectum or an incision). Popularly called "magic eye".

Endoscopic surgery Surgical procedures accessing body cavities such as the chest or abdomen through an endoscope, causing smaller wounds, less internal disturbance, and allowing much shorter stays in hospital. Also called "keyhole", minimal access, or minimally invasive surgery.

Episodic care Medical attention restricted to one single procedure or episode of illness (as opposed to continuing care)

Hysterectomy Removal of the uterus

In-patients Patients admitted to hospital who stay one or more nights

Local Medical Committee A committee elected by family doctors to represent their interests to the health authority

Mortality Death rate

Out-patients Patients seen at hospital but not admitted to a bed either as a day-case or as an in-patient

Primary care Medical and nursing care provided in the community from family doctors' surgeries or health centres, and other sources of health professional advice to which people have direct access, such as chemists, dentists, and opticians

Referral Temporary transfer of responsibility for a patient by one professional to another professional for specialist advice or a specialised procedure

Secondary care Medical and nursing care provided in local hospitals (normally District General Hospitals) by referral from primary care

Tertiary care Medical and nursing care outside the usual range of a District General Hospital, normally by referral from a DGH specialist. Examples are neurosurgical units, burns units, renal (kidney) units, and thoracic surgery units for open heart operations and operations on the lungs

*A*bbreviations

BMA	British Medical Association
DGH	District General Hospital
GNP	Gross National Product
GP	General Practitioner
FHSA	Family Health Services Authority (formerly Executive Councils, then Family Practitioner Committees (FPCs)
HA	Health Authority
MPU	Medical Practitioners' Union
NHS	National Health Service
OECD	Organization for Economic and Cultural Development
QUANGO	Quasi-nongovernmental organisation
SHA	Socialist Health Association

Learning Resources
Centre